THE KNOWLEDGE AND THE POWER

THE KNOWLEDGE
AND THE POWER

Reflections on the History of Science

IVAN TOLSTOY

CANONGATE

First published in Great Britain in 1990
by Canongate Publishing Ltd, Edinburgh.

Copyright © Ivan Tolstoy

British Library Cataloguing in Publication Data
Tolstoy, Ivan *1923–*
The knowledge and the power:
reflections on the history of science.
1. Science, history
I. Title
509

ISBN 0-86241-277-3

Typeset by Bookworm Typesetting Ltd, 9a Gayfield Square,
Edinburgh.
Printed and bound by Billings and Sons Ltd, Worcester.

This book is dedicated to the memory of Elisabeth Shuvalov. I would also like to thank Margie Tolstoy for her patience, encouragement and advice.

Contents

But where shall wisdom be found?
and where is the place of understanding?
Job 28, 12

Preface

From the beginnings, the business of science has been pictured in at least two ways.

For some it has been a quest for knowledge, unblemished by thoughts of power. That is how Pythagoras, Darwin or Einstein saw it — as a religion, an art and a way of life. By no means limited to men and women of genius, such commitment requires a philosophical turn of mind, integrity and no great worldly ambitions. This is *pure science*, the organizing of our sense of wonder, knowledge for its own sake — an expression of what Einstein called our holy curiosity. Like poetry, art, philosophy or theology, it is a true measure of our humanity.

For others science has been a search for power — power over nature, people and nations; a search for antibiotics, nuclear reactors and moonshots. *Pure* scientists refer to this as *applied science*, a label to which they affix, more often than not, a hint of disavowal. But for the seekers after power it embodies, ultimately, the real — the *sole* — purpose of knowledge.

Science as knowledge and science as power: *like all our dichotomies, it is highly simplistic*. The two views are not so much antithetical as complementary. Often they have fed on each other, pure science leading to new technology and new tools, to better instruments, and these in turn creating new knowledge. 'The high and the low', says the Tao, 'rest upon each other.'

This interaction — the knowledge-power feedback loop — has, to various degrees, always been with us. Weak in classical Greece, it came alive in the sixteenth and seventeenth centuries, and grew rapidly during the Enlightenment. In our century it has blossomed as never before — together with a prevalent, largely unexamined *faith* which sees pure science as leading inevitably to new technologies, and hence to industrial might and economic prosperity. Even the purest, most abstract fields, like high energy physics or number theory, may be viewed in this light — a philosophy encapsulated by such institutional truths as 'today's basic science is tomorrow's technology'.

Our society is more interested in power than in knowledge *per se*: in a materialist world, a world of economic and political strife, of fear and confrontation, applied science is queen. Yet pure and applied science *are* symbiotic; and, to some extent, those who run our society believe this. Prodded by a variety of science lobbies, they keep the faith and see to it that large sums are lavished on pure ('basic') science: three billion dollars to map our genetic blueprint (the human genome), seven billions for a new giant accelerator (the SSC or Superconducting Supercollider), two billions a year for the National Science Foundation. The motive behind this munificence is power; the bottom line is economic, military and political clout. Some scientists may be driven by holy curiosity, but their paymasters serve a different god.

The ties between science and technology, between knowledge and power, are, in truth, subtle, chaotic and far from clear. Everyone talks about them, but no one really understands them.

Like most scientists of my generation I started out, in the late 1940s, as a naive idealist. As a young geophysicist, my work seemed far removed from newborn weapons of mass slaughter, unrelated to the paranoia and power-plays of nations. My heroes were quiet men like Darwin, Einstein or Mendeleyev — people whose lives had been devoted to the study of a mysterious, fascinating universe of fossils, galaxies and atoms, a world waiting out there to be discovered. It appeared axiomatic that there had to be such a thing as the truth, that knowledge thereof would make us wise, that science could lead us to it. There was, after all, the scientific method, and this offered a royal road to knowledge. But truth turned out to be a more slippery thing than my teachers had led me to believe. Those who think about such matters professionally — the philosophers of science — tell us that the concept of science as the pursuit of truth is now obsolescent.[1] They now add, for good measure, that there is no scientific method. Mathematicians have discovered *chaos*; the world is, in essential ways, unpredictable — it is full of effects we can never trace to causes. To top it all, as an aftermath of the Second World War, science became an affluent enterprise, and affluence has transformed it. Supported by and beholden to society on a scale undreamt of by previous generations, it has become thoroughly institutionalized. And so, as if the pursuit of scientific understanding were not of itself hard enough, we are now, all of us, scientists, technocrats and lay people alike, faced with the problem of distinguishing knowledge from institutional truth, — of separating the wheat from the chaff.

The organization of my material reflects these facts, and requires a few words of explanation. I start with a chapter on Einstein and the birth of modern physics; had I followed a chronological order this should have come after Chapter 11. But Einstein is very special; he was a unique combination of supreme talent, integrity and human decency. What better way to begin a book on science than with the portrait of a man who embodied all that is best in the enterprise — especially when this also helps to illuminate the intellectual revolution which changed the face of physics at the beginning of our century? Chapter 2 offers a concise view of the theory of chaos — a development of the last thirty years which has completely altered our perceptions of the universe and environment we inhabit; since history and science themselves appear to proceed chaotically — in the literal, modern sense of the word — it seemed sensible to introduce the concept before proceeding further. Chapter 3 is a summary/introduction to the philosophy of science. Again it appeared important to *define one's terms* at the beginning of the book: it would be unreasonable not to recount, early on, efforts to describe what science *is*. Hopefully these introductory chapters will help the reader approach the rest with open eyes — forewarned that science is not easily defined, that it does not necessarily deal with simple cause and effect relationships, that, created by people, it is embedded in a historical context, and that one must remain sceptical of all theories of its history and evolution. This being said, the remaining, largely historical chapters are offered in chronological sequence. The resultant, slightly spurious tidiness is, to some extent, counterbalanced by the early chapters as well as by examples and brief biographical sketches — emphasizing that science did not develop in an orderly, systematic way. Its evolution has in fact been rather anarchic, unplanned and subject to chaotic historical and individual influences. A felicitous analogy here is due to Feyerabend: he likens the growth of science to the acquiring of language by a child — an unsystematic, playful, yet miraculously effective process. If it follows a method, we have still to find it.[2]

[1] J.R. Ravetz, *Scientific Knowledge and its Social Problems*, Clarendon Press, 1971.
[2] Paul Feyerabend, *Against Method*, Verso, London, 1978.

CHAPTER ONE

The Age of Einstein

Northern France is an open land, still and flat, and tinged with sadness. There are too many cemeteries here, too many neat rows of white crosses — memories of a world war which blasted farms, villages and towns into oblivion and turned a peaceful countryside into a hell. The land is long since healed, the soil neatly cultivated. Along the roadsides and in the pastures are wildflowers — bluebells, daisies, buttercups, azure forget-me-nots. From May till September the hedgerows and fields are dotted with blood-red poppies, whose papery petals seem too fragile to withstand even the gentlest summer breezes of Picardy and Flanders. Yet they last the summer, splashes of crimson on green or ochre, inspiring generations of painters and gladdening the traveller's eye. In the autumn, with the first cold weather, they disappear. But the crosses of Flanders, Verdun and the Somme remain — dotted white lines on acres of grass, stretching through the gentle morning mists or under the caress of an evening sun, mute, infinitely sad reminders of mankind's folly. Here lies the acquiescent generation led, in 1914, to pointless slaughter — the German Crown Prince's 'bright and jolly war'.

The Enlightenment, the American and French Revolutions, the Industrial Revolution, the writings of Marx, the huge advances of science and technology had unleashed great forces. Tragically, there was no one of sufficient stature, power and influence to help Europe ride out the storms of change. Those fields of white crosses spell out, as nothing else can, the tragedy of a generation which went out to die for the blunders, corruption and inept power plays of vain, ambitious old men overtaken by forces they did not understand.

Throughout recent history science, philosophy and technology had led and fuelled revolutionary transformations. It would,

1

however, take a new, brave kind of historian to try to trace the subtle, intimate and excessively complex interrelations between knowledge, power, politics and war. But regardless of whether these can ever be truly reconstructed, there is no doubt that the First World War — and its sequels — were the product of intense, accelerating changes — changes so rapid and deep that governments, deluded politicians and foolish monarchs were simply unable to cope.

Change feeds on change. While at the turn of the century social and political storms were battering the world and later, while millions were dying in the mud and trenches of the First World War, a small band of men and women were making discoveries which would, in the long term, alter society in ways spectacular and astonishing, and give mankind powers far greater than any dreamt of by even the most megalomaniac turn-of-the-century ruler. Largely insulated from direct involvement in the surrounding chaos — by age, nationality, health, occupation — these people worked alone in universities or in small groups, often against considerable odds, driven by the clarity and brilliance of an inner vision — Becquerel, Marie and Pierre Curie, Bohr, Rutherford, Einstein. A few, like Moseley, died young, cut down before their prime by the obscenity of war. Others, like Planck, lived through two world wars and died old men, out-distanced by the progress they had set in motion. Some lived to see the dawn of Big Science and bemoan it. The greatest among them, the giant, the individualist and genius whose contributions have dominated modern science, our twentieth century Newton, was Albert Einstein.

He was born in Germany, in Ulm, in 1879, the year Maxwell died. A quiet, introspective child, he was a late developer; he did not talk till he was almost three. In mathematics and Latin his performance at the Munich *gymnasium* was brilliant, but in other subjects it was erratic. A teacher of Greek is reported to have told him that he never would amount to much. Perceptive souls, like his Uncle Jacob, glimpsed hidden depths in the boy. But his early stimulation in science seems to have been haphazard — a gift of a compass from his father, at the age of five, a geometry book at the age of twelve from Uncle Jacob (he would later refer to it as his 'holy geometry book'), popular science books and discussions with Max Talmey, a medical student and friend of the family. Much later, Einstein was to assert that he had been a backward youth; to this, with characteristic modesty, he ascribed his success with the theory of relativity: ' . . . my intellectual development was retarded, as a result of which I began to wonder about space and time only when I had already grown up. Naturally, I could go deeper into the problem than a child with normal abilities.'[1]

His parents, Hermann and Pauline Einstein, moved to Italy in 1894. Unhappy, unable to accept the absurd, quasi-military discipline of a German *gymnasium*, he engineered his release — without a diploma — and rejoined his parents. Eventually, he made it to Switzerland and via a cantonal school in Aarau, to the Zurich Polytechnic which he entered in 1896. Here too his performance was chequered. He abhorred exams, cut lectures and spent much time reading the great works of science and philosophy. And he mastered on his own Maxwell's theory, which was not yet being taught at the university. His classic comment on those years was: 'One had to cram all this stuff into one's mind for the examinations, whether one liked it or not. This coercion had such a deterring effect on me that, after I passed the final examination, I found consideration of any scientific problems distasteful for an entire year'.

The time following graduation was a dark one; rebuffed in his efforts at finding an academic position, he took odd jobs, like tutoring physics (at three francs an hour). After a year, though, his interest in science returned and he wrote his first paper (on capillarity, 1901). He may have been saved from total despair, maybe even oblivion, by his friend Marcel Grossman, a fellow student and brilliant mathematician, who arranged a position for him as a probationary technical expert, third class, at the Patent Office in Berne (1902). The job was not taxing and Einstein's life-style, simple and uncluttered, left him time for his own, private work. In these unlikely surroundings, his genius came to fruition. In 1905 he completed six extraordinary pieces of research. In fact, 1905 was to be one of science's great vintage years; the year in which Einstein published (or submitted) six papers in *Annalen der Physik*, a brief slice in time as important in the history of science as Newton's legendary two years in Colsterworth during the great plague.

Of these papers one, Einstein's PhD. thesis, discussed methods for determining atomic and molecular dimensions by measuring diffusion and viscosity in liquids. Two others dealt with Brownian motion, i.e., with random motions of a small dust or pollen particle in a drop of fluid, as seen under a microscope. Einstein demonstrated that this agitation was a direct manifestation of the impacts of individual molecules in perpetual motion within the liquid — another proof, if necessary, of the atomistic nature of matter. These were fine papers and would by themselves have earned Einstein a significant niche in the history of physics. But the other three were far more: they were revolutionary.

First was his famous 'photoelectric paper'. To appreciate it, one must go back a few years to 1900, when this particular revolution began. It started when Max Planck (1858-1947) offered an explanation of discrepancies observed in the glow of a so-called black-body — an idealized chunk of hot iron. It had been discovered that existing formulae (the Wien law) did not work as one got towards the red and infra-red end of the spectrum. Planck produced a formula that *did* work, i.e., he fitted the observations with a mathematical curve. Not content with this, he looked for a physical explanation; and the only one he could find was that energy, like matter, comes in bits, or discontinuous *quanta*. Energy, said Planck, was not, as had been surmised, a continuous thing. As water seems continuous to our senses while being in fact a collection of a great many discrete, individual particles or molecules, so energy can only be given or taken in discrete steps or quanta. This was a bold and visionary step — a revolution was born, and it transformed the face of science.*

Einstein's paper dealt with a somewhat different problem: the knocking of electrons out of the surface of a metal by light. Only a few years after J.J. Thomson had demonstrated the existence of electrons (1897), Lenard in Germany had started experiments on the ejection of electrons from metals by light. This *photoelectric effect* did not fit into the scheme of Maxwell's

---

* There is still some argument as to the extent to which Planck saw these quanta as physical or as mere computational devices. This, however, would take us too far afield.

theory. In particular, the energy of the electrons emitted was determined not, as one might have expected, by the intensity of the light but by its colour. Einstein showed that if one assumed light to consist of discrete packets of energy or *protons* similar to Planck's quanta, the effect could be explained. This was a stroke of genius comparable to (and perhaps exceeding) Planck's and one for which he, too, would eventually receive the Nobel prize. Both papers, Einstein's (1905) and Planck's (1901) caused a considerable stir. The more profound consequences of this work, though, were not yet apparent; the philosophic and scientific harvest was to outrun the dreams of even the most imaginative scientists, including Einstein himself. It was to lead to a profound and elegant description of the atomic world: the *quantum theory* of matter.

Next were two papers broaching a subject which would, eventually, be regarded as uniquely his: the *theory of relativity*. There are two theories here: the *special* and the *general*. The 1905 papers laid the foundations of the *special* theory of relativity. The most famous is the one titled '*On the Electrodynamics of Moving Bodies*' — a title which, in the annals of science is as famous as the *Origin of Species* or Newton's *Principia*, famous because it totally changed our views of space and time and because it revolutionized natural philosophy by accomplishing what philosophers had never ventured to try: wedding space and time into a single entity, *space-time*.

Einstein produced this, his first great paper on relativity, at a critical moment, when science's views on space and time had run into trouble. Maxwell's equations appeared to imply that, since light propagates as waves, there must be a medium to carry them. As water waves need a water surface to travel on, and sound waves need a fluid to sustain them, so light waves appeared to require something — a medium which had not yet been detected, but which had received a name: *the ether*. But then, just as motion through water or air are easily perceived, just so motion through the ether, it seemed, had to be at least detectable: the Earth was moving in space and it *should* be possible to measure its movement through this medium. Using highly refined optical apparatus, the Americans Michelson and Morley, in the 1880s, had made several attempts to do so, and had drawn a blank. Lorentz, in Holland, offered an explanation: bodies, he said, contracted as they moved through the ether in such a way as to make the motion undetectable. This hypothesis, however, did not quite square with Maxwell's equations. Henri Poincaré then attempted to remove the difficulty by ingenious mathematics; indeed he all but arrived at the theory of relativity — he certainly obtained some of Einstein's formulae. Yet he failed to put all the pieces together. It was Einstein who did this, by an independent route, a route resting squarely on his physical intuition.

To begin, he said, one should accept two principles. First, that it is impossible to define, in absolute terms, uniform motion through space. Second, that light travels through space with a constant, definite speed which does not depend upon the motion of source and receiver. Such was the physical basis of Einstein's special relativity; this, it turned out, was enough to make the ether idea superfluous and to remove the logical difficulties which had puzzled physicists, such as the negative outcome of the Michelson-Morley experiments (whereas Einstein did not refer to these in his 1905 papers, he was aware of their existence; but their direct influence on his early work was slight — a discussion of this point will be found in Pais' biography).[2] It also preserved intact Maxwell's equations.

Like Newton's laws, these were simple, straightforward principles and, like them, their precise mathematical formulation had far-reaching effects. Time, wedded to space in a single space-time continuum, became relative. And, as Einstein showed in his second 1905 relativity paper, a direct corollary was that mass and energy were equivalent: $E=mc^2$ — energy equalled mass times the square of the speed of light, perhaps the most famous physics formula of all time (it even surfaced in a 1982 pop song). Mass and energy were manifestations of *the same thing* and were, in principle, interchangeable. We know today that whenever, in an atomic nucleus, particles are joined together by subatomic force fields, the mass of the combination is less than the sum of the masses of these particles. The difference is accounted for in terms of the energy stored by the new structure; this, the *binding energy*, is what is released in all nuclear devices. In this way, then, Einstein's 1905 work led both to nuclear bombs and to power stations. And, without Einstein's special relativity, the accelerators at

Fermilab, CERN and Serpukhov would never work, their multi-million dollar technology could never be designed — for the theory has provided, along with so much else, the means of understanding the behaviour of particles moving at the high speeds reached in these machines. Mass, it turns out, is not constant; it increases with velocity until, as one nears the speed of light, it tends to become infinite: the speed of light is, in a real sense, unattainable by any object with mass. Modern particle physics could not have sprung into existence without relativity; nor, indeed, would the behaviour of atoms and their nuclei be comprehensible.

After these papers, which appeared when Einstein was twenty-six, recognition of this phenomenal young man was, one would think, assured. Yet it took singularly long. A handful of top people, such as Planck, Born and Infeld recognized his genius; but most of the older generation came to terms with him slowly, if at all. Only in 1909, after a short stint as *privat-dozent* (a sort of unpaid lecturer) at the University of Berne, did he finally cease to be a low-ranking Swiss civil servant, abandon his post as patent examiner, and accept an associate professorship from the Zurich Polytechnic. From what Banesh Hoffman calls 'a scientist of minor academic qualifications who had launched an obscure theory on the world . . . the man who failed to fit or to conform, the disrespector of professors, the dropper of conversational bricks, the awkward Jewish customer . . .'[3] he turned into a fully fledged academic at one of the better European institutions. By 1911 he had moved to Prague, in 1913 back to Zurich and in 1914 to Berlin where he was to stay until 1933. Despite the roving, despite the 1914-18 war, these too were remarkably creative years for the young Einstein. It was then that he conceived the *general theory of relativity*..

This was the third major revolution in physics during the first decades of the twentieth century — and it was uniquely Einstein's. According to some, the general theory is the great man's greatest piece of work. Mathematically more difficult, physically more radical than the special theory, it took years to mature. The original inspiration apparently came to him in 1907 when, musing in his patent office in Berne, he suddenly saw that 'if a person falls freely he will not feel his own weight' — an idea he would later describe as 'the happiest thought of my life'. A first paper in 1911 stated the logical conclusion of this happiest thought, i.e., Einstein's *principle of equivalence*, which says that a force-measuring instrument responds to acceleration in the same way as it does to the pull of gravity. This allowed Einstein to predict such curious effects as the bending of starlight as it passes near the sun, and the reddening of light emitted by massive stars — years before either was measured. This was fundamental; but it was not enough. What he did next was to express the principle in general form so that it said, in effect, that all arbitrarily accelerated systems were equivalent to gravitational fields generated by distributions of mass. To express this formally and rigorously was difficult, but with help from mathematically skilled friends, notably Marcel Grossmann, Einstein succeeded. This theory did something that in classical, Newtonian terms, could not even be conceived: it explained the forces of gravitation in terms of the intrinsic geometry of the space in which we live. Not only are space and time wedded into a single four-dimensional space-time continuum as they had been in special relativity but, says the general theory, this continuum is not Euclidean. A popular subterfuge for visualizing such a universe is to shift one's attention to a space of fewer dimensions. Imagine, for instance, a two-dimensional world as the surface of a lumpy table, with depressions scattered here and there. Consider then a billiard ball launched at speed along the surface. Between depressions the table is flat and the ball travels in a straight line: in the absence of forces, the space is Euclidean and Newton's first law is obeyed. Elsewhere, the ball is deflected by the depressions; it does not travel in a straight line; its curved trajectory is called a *geodesic* (shortest path) of this two-dimensional world. The deflections may be interpreted as due to the attraction of a distribution of mass (Newton) or as the result of the curvature of space (Einstein). Try then to imagine a similar situation in a four-dimensional (space-time) universe, and you have the gist of general relativity. Light does not travel in straight lines but follows curved paths or geodesics; gravity is not, as Newton postulated, action-at-a-distance but rather the manifestation of the warp or curvature of space-time. The famed inverse square law, on the other hand, is shown to follow *approximately* from the theory of general relativity for gravitational forces (space-time curvatures) that are not too great. Thus Newton's theory of planetary motions, of lunar dynamics and satellites remains good enough for most practical purposes. But when one approaches too closely a massive body, the warping of space-time introduces substantial departures from the Newtonian model. In 1915 Einstein succeeded, this way, in explaining a slow rotation (precession) of the orbit of Mercury, which classical Newtonian mechanics had been powerless to account for.

Someday, one may hope, in a gentler and more civilized world, history will treat the First World War as an embarassing and shameful footnote, and the period 1915-17 will be recorded chiefly as the years during which the general theory of relativity saw the light of day: it is, certainly, one of the major intellectual masterpieces of all time. It provides a glimpse into the nature of gravitation and gives a framework for understanding the universe as a whole. The consequences of the theory are still incompletely explored; but it has, most definitely, given mankind its first reasonable views on the large-scale structure of the cosmos, its origins and history. It has permitted the mathematical description of whole worlds or *cosmological models*. Einstein spent many years constructing, exploring and refining new, mathematical universes.

At the same time, astronomers were vastly increasing our perceptions of the universe. In 1924 the American astronomer Edwin Hubble showed that the galaxies were at very great distances from ours (the Milky Way), extending the perceived dimensions of the universe to billions of light-years. In 1929 he made a particularly striking discovery: the universe was expanding, a fact which he deduced from the reddening of light from distant galaxies (the galactic red shift). Just as the blast of a horn changes pitch as a car passes us and begins to recede, so the light from a rapidly receding object like a star or a galaxy turns reddish as it races away. Distant galaxies are redder than near ones: Hubble concluded that the rate of recession increases with distance. Gratifyingly, Einstein's general equations could be made to accommodate such a universe.

During Einstein's life, the general theory of relativity was recognized as a masterpiece, an accomplishment of singular beauty. But the size of the effects it predicted seemed small and difficult to verify. And so, it remained, for a long time, outside the mainstream of physics. A few cosmologists and mathematicians and, of course, Einstein himself, chipped patiently away at its difficult equations. For a long time the chief excitement was elsewhere — in quantum physics and special relativity. These combined to generate in physics, chemistry and astrophysics an activity which was feverish, enthusiastic and truly international. Chief among the groups that helped illuminate the structure of the atom were one in Copenhagen, dominated and inspired by Niels Bohr, and another in Britain, at the Cavendish laboratory, led by Ernest Rutherford.

The emergence of an accurate theory of the atom during the early decades of this century is another of the great intellectual adventure stories of our civilization. It had all begun, of course, long, long ago with Democritos of Abdera. But scientific *evidence* for the atom came, strictly speaking, only at the dawn of the nineteenth century with Dalton, Proust and Richter. Mendeleyev's table, in 1871, threw a sharp light on the matter: any model of the atom was going to have to explain the regular periodicities of the table. By the end of the century, also, atoms were known to emit or absorb accurately defined colours of light, or *spectral lines*, the so-called emission and absorption spectra; while these were actually used to identify elements, their reason for being was not understood at all. And another new atomic phenomenon, *radioactivity*, discovered by Becquerel and studied by Marie and Pierre Curie, was enormously exciting and equally mysterious. Clearly the dynamics of the atom had to be unlike anything physics had dealt with before. It was all to fall neatly into place, in a matter of three decades or so, thanks to Planck's and Einstein's ideas about quanta — and the resulting development of *quantum mechanics*.

In 1911 Rutherford had conceived the atom as a miniature solar system with a heavy, charged nucleus as sun and negative electrons as planets, held together by electric rather than gravitational forces. This was an ingenious idea; but it had two major faults. First of all, according to Maxwell's equations, such electrons would have to radiate electromagnetic waves, lose energy and spiral in to the nucleus: the atom would collapse. Secondly it did not explain the discreteness of emission and absorption spectra. Bohr then pointed out that both difficulties were resolved by making the *ad hoc* assumption that electrons were constrained to stable orbits, radiating and absorbing energy only in discrete quanta, as they jumped from one orbit to another (1913). The nature of the constraint was not clear, but the model clarified a great many observations. The discreteness of the spectral lines was thereby explained and was extended to X-rays by Moseley (1887-1915); it was seen to be analogous to the differences in pitch between strings of various lengths: the atom was ruled by integers. Pythagoras' music of the spheres was mirrored in the intimate structure of the atom. Bohr's idea was pure genius: 'The highest form of musicality in the sphere of thought', said Einstein — who also contributed to the theory, showing how the particle model of light explained the absorption and emission of discrete spectra through collisions between photons and electrons.

De Broglie in 1924, then Schrödinger and Born removed some of the arbitrariness of Bohr's model by interpreting particles in terms of waves — waves which were not real matter waves, but waves of probability travelling in abstract spaces. This, properly speaking, marked the birth of the quantum theory of the atom — the modern view of matter. It was to be perfected during the next decade, with remarkable speed and brilliance, by Schrödinger, Born, Heisenberg, Dirac, Pauli and others. Dirac's mathematical work, in particular, amalgamating quantum principles with Einstein's special relativity, made in 1928 a strange and wonderful prediction: it foretold the existence of a mirror world, a world of *antimatter* with negatively charged protons (anti-protons), positive electrons (positrons), and so on. No one believed Dirac, at first. But the existence of the positron was soon confirmed: Carl Anderson found it in 1932, in cosmic ray studies. The quantum theory gave us a thorough, detailed and fastidiously accurate understanding of the atom. It also demolished some of the philosophical complacency of the nineteenth-century view of the world by destroying determinism.

The determinism and concreteness of the Newtonian world was demolished, largely, because the theory said, in effect, that we cannot disentangle ourselves, our methods of thinking and observing, from the world we study. A detached, *God's* view, if it exists at all, is unattainable to the human mind.

Our inability to step beyond ourselves and view the world objectively, our self-entanglement as it were, is due to two major causes.

The first, and perhaps the more subtle, concerns the way we think. It is wrong, says the quantum theory, to visualize the fundamental constituents of matter, like electrons or nuclei, as simple particles of some kind of unyielding, primal stuff. In fact, says the theory — and experiment confirms this — they can behave either as particles, or as waves: the particle and wave concepts are said to be *complementary*. Depending upon what we do to matter, we bring one or the other of these attributes to the fore. In an electron microscope, we use the wave properties of electrons; in a Geiger counter we detect individual collisions, i.e., we use the particle properties of radiation. Herein is the final reconciliation of two opposing theories of light, the harmonizing of Newton and Huygens, of Maxwell's equations and Einstein's photons. This *complementarity* appears almost of the same ilk as many other of our dualities and value judgments: darkness and light, good and evil, beauty and ugliness, intuition and thinking. These concepts all seem to involve opposites which, while apparently irreconcilable, cannot in fact exist without each other and are, ultimately, but dual aspects of a single truth. As a general concept, complementarity is far from new; a cornerstone of Buddhist philosophy, it had, more recently, surfaced as the foundation of Jung's psychology. The need to think in archetypal, complementary ways is, without a doubt, a characteristic of the human mind. In our efforts to understand, to order the universe to our liking, we end up with a reflection of ourselves: as Eddington once put it, the footprints on the sand may be our own.

The second way in which we are enmeshed in the world we study is more direct: it concerns the manner in which we observe. To be 'observed' an object must interact with other objects — with particles of matter, such as electrons, or of light (photons). Indeed we only see things because photons are bouncing off them and hitting our retina. If the observed object itself is very small and light, like a subatomic particle, it will suffer some kind of recoil or deflection. With an apology to complementarity, one thinks, for instance, of the collisions of billiard balls; the object is affected by being collided with, i.e., by being *seen*. The very act of observing an electron disturbs it in ways we cannot, in general, foresee or correct for. This, clearly, is an insight of great scope for it tells us that we can never attain complete certainty in our knowledge of matter. The precise mathematical statement of this fact is due to Heisenberg (1927): it is his famous *uncertainty principle*. This tells us, specifically, that if we measure one quantity, like the position of a particle we must, inevitably, lose sight of another, such as its speed: a photon bouncing off a particle may tell us where it was, but the recoil has changed its speed and direction of motion by an unknown amount.

Nature is fundamentally and irreducibly indeterministic and, as the mathematical development of the theory demonstrated, our predictions are only statistically valid; we deal always with *probable* behaviour, never with certainties. The theory shows, though, that in dealing with very large numbers of atoms, as we do in our everyday (macroscopic) world, the probability of normal, Newtonian behaviour becomes so overwhelming as to bring us back, seemingly, to determinism.

The theory led, almost immediately, to a host of ramifications, new applications and insights. One curious result deserves special mention: particles with mass, such as electrons, turned out to have a property called *spin*. Here ordinary language fails but, roughly speaking, the property of spin is analogous to what we think of when we talk of a spinning ball or top. The arithmetic of the theory demonstrates that such particles are not necessarily 'really' spinning; it is a mathematical property — the word *spin* is an image, and not an entirely adequate one; but it is close enough. It was just another glimpse of a strange new world, a world of properties for which our language has no words and for which our sense perceptions, our everyday experience and common sense had not prepared us.

Well into the 1930s the centre of gravity of this work was in Western Europe and the British Isles; after the Nazi madness appeared there occurred a massive migration of intellectuals to Britain and the United States. American science received a huge boost; from a modestly financed, somewhat second-rate enterprise, it was to become, after 1940, the world's most powerful knowledge factory. Activity in the physical sciences during 1930-40 was frenzied; it seems as if the stimulation by the great ideas of the first quarter century had been so strong that nothing could arrest the explosion of knowledge. Despite the restlessness and anxiety of those years, a small group of British, German, French, Danish, Russian physicists and chemists kept their investigations going through thick and thin. Many were poorly paid and all were, by modern standards, inadequately financed; yet with undimmed enthusiasm they spent most of the 1930s describing and studying the *nucleus* of the atom. The single-mindedness of these men and women was amazing, even frightening, leading at times to such views as Rutherford's haughty: 'There is physics and the rest is stamp-collecting'. Mistakenly or not, they felt they were getting at the very roots of the universe and, mesmerized by the idea, few, if any, dreamt of fame, power or money. Nor, apparently, did they waste much thought on the long-term practical implications of their work.

It was during the last decade before the Second World War that the neutron was discovered at the Cavendish by James Chadwick (1932) and investigated by the great Enrico Fermi (1934) in Italy (and, later, by Lise Meitner and Otto Hahn in Germany). It seemed established, by the mid-1930s, that the nucleus consisted of a small number of irreducible particles. While, like all such entities, they exhibited the usual particle-wave duality, it was generally agreed to refer to them as particles or *nucleons*. They were: the *neutron*, so called because it had no electric charge, the *proton* which seemed to be little more than a neutron with a positive electric charge and, of course, the electron, almost two thousand times less massive — the basic unit of electrical charge. In addition theory predicted, and experiment eventually confirmed, the existence of *positrons*, and of *mesons* — the latter acting like a nuclear glue holding protons and neutrons together in the nucleus. The picture was relatively simple; it appeared to account well for the known properties of matter. It predicted, too, that very heavy elements, whose nuclei consist of many protons and neutrons, would be unstable: the meson glue was no longer enough to keep the electrical repulsion between protons in check, and the nucleus tended to disintegrate. This explained, neatly, the phenomenon of natural radioactivity, and its concentration in elements at the end of the periodic table. Just before the beginning of the war, in 1939, the fission of uranium was discovered by a German team (Meitner, Hahn, Strassman and Frisch). A remarkable feature of this disintegration was that, triggered by neutrons, it produced yet more neutrons, leading to the possibility of a chain reaction . . .

Thus, in the first forty years of the twentieth century, our vision of the physical world changed radically and irretrievably. Atoms could behave like solid matter or like waves, they were made of particles with strange top-like properties, with nuclei which could disintegrate spontaneously and, perhaps, set up chains of disintegration themselves. The implications of all this were unclear — some, indeed, are still being debated. For many, the most interesting implication of all this new knowledge was, and still is, philosophical. For, if we think about quantum theory, about Heisenberg's uncertainty principle, about the wave properties of matter, one conclusion stands out clearly: the very concept of understanding has been changed. Quantum mechanics and relativity took us into new spheres of thought; they taught us that our senses are poor guides in tackling the deeper questions of space, time and matter. While this startled scientists at the beginning of the century, it no longer shocks us for we have understood that our intuitive ideas of what is possible and what is not — our common sense — are a result of the conditioning of our mind by sense experiences. The world of these is, precisely, the world of classical Newtonian science: not unnaturally, physics had first applied itself to this domain — which, after all, is the only one accessible to direct perception. But in exploring realms into which our senses cannot penetrate, they offer us no guidance; and thus, when science looks at the very small (atoms, quantum mechanics) or the very large (cosmos, general relativity) it can appear, at first, that things are topsy-turvy. *We have had to change our ideas of what understanding consists.* As Bohr said: 'When it comes to atoms, language can only be used as in poetry. The poet, too, is not nearly so concerned with describing facts as with creating images.' The same is true of cosmological models, curved spaces and exploding universes. Images and analogies are the key; as Bronowski once put it, what lies below the visible world is a play of images.[4] And behind it all is the tyranny of words. From this we escape, partially, through the use of mathematics for, to those who have mastered it, this is both a precise and an infinitely rich language. One line of mathematical symbols can contain a whole universe — a description of which in words would fill whole libraries and never be so accurate. Words are inadequate, their tyranny *is* real. Not you, not I, not Einstein could interpret the universe in terms wholly related to our senses. Not that it is incomprehensible; no. But we must learn to ignore our preconceptions concerning space, time and matter, abandon the uses of everyday language and resort to metaphor. We must try to think like poets.

Such views, or something like them, are acceptable to modern scientists. At first, though, they were less so; many found it difficult to abandon the clockwork determinism of the Newtonian universe. Physicists had, of course, long ago understood the role of experimental error — they had accepted the implications of Gauss' bell-shaped curve; no measurement was error-free and this, they knew, cast a shadow of uncertainty on one's knowledge of even a Newtonian world. But, until the advent of modern physics, it remained possible to conceive indefinite improvements in experimental technique leading to equally indefinite refinements in knowledge. In the Newtonian world uncertainty was a limitation of ours, not Nature's. Quantum theory told a different story; it imposed absolute bounds upon our knowledge: you could refine your techniques all you wanted, eventually you ran into a wall, measurements failed you. Indeterminism was part of nature, it was intrinsic to the structure of the world. You could only deal with the probability of a particle being here, there, anywhere; and if you determined its position to a high degree of accuracy, you lost all knowledge of its velocity, or *vice-versa*. Einstein, in particular, never reconciled himself to this; he never accepted the full implications of the uncertainty principle. For years, an epic argument went on between him and the Copenhagen school, Bohr taking the position that nature was ruled by chance, Einstein conceding the beauty and success of the modern theory but viewing it, nevertheless, as temporary and incomplete: for him, its indeterminism was not fundamental. It merely reflected our ignorance: God, his classic saying went, did not play dice with the universe. But, as he grew older, his objections were overriden one by one and he withdrew from the mainstream of atomic and nuclear physics. In 1933, fleeing the Nazis, he moved to Oxford, then to Princeton. Here he immersed himself, more and more, in the elusive search for a unified theory of electromagnetism and gravitation, for a last, sweeping, all-embracing generalization of his theories of relativity. Several times he thought he had found it; always, though, flaws were discovered; always, the dream escaped him.

Einstein was a solitary, private man. Throughout his life, he subordinated his relationships with people to the imperatives of his work. His first marriage, to Mileva, a Serbian fellow-student from his Zurich days, ended in what Banesh Hoffmann calls 'an amicable divorce' (1919). His second wife, Elsa, died in 1936. The final, lonely decades of his life were spent in Princeton. While he acquired US citizenship, it is unlikely that he ever felt fully at home there. Americans tend to be gregarious, he was unsociable, almost a recluse; and his political views — a straightforward and idealistic blend of pacifism, anarchism and internationalism — did little to endear him to the establishment. Like all of us, Einstein was not always consistent; he admired Gandhi and considered him the greatest political figure of our time; yet, in 1939, he signed the letter to Roosevelt suggesting early development of nuclear bombs. Yet in all this he remained strangely unsullied; the world forgave him his ambiguities. Maybe it was his intellectual stature, or his obvious, whole-hearted commitment to those ideals of peace and justice our society so often mocks. Perhaps it was simply his remarkable combination of transparent honesty and modesty: 'I know a little about Nature, but hardly anything about men' said he, refusing the presidency of Israel.

Einstein had held, at various times, four different citizenships: German, Swiss, Austro-Hungarian and American. During the hysterical McCarthyism of the early 1950s he was viciously attacked, and thought once more of emigrating; evidently, he changed his mind. Very likely he simply felt too old and tired; perhaps, too, he had resigned himself to human folly. For that matter, where else was there to go? And, against the backdrop of creation, of stars, of galaxies and atoms, of vast cosmic spaces wherein his mind so liked to roam, the problems of nationality and politics were petty ones indeed. Yet, despite the esotericism of his inner world, he never forgot his fellow men, never lost his idealism and social consciousness.

Einstein's last public act, in April 1955, was to sign the Russell-Einstein declaration beseeching all nations to settle their disputes by peaceful means and to renounce the use of nuclear weapons. But, as his last written words put it, he knew that 'Political passions, aroused everywhere, demand their victims' (11th April).

On 15th April he was taken to hospital, in great pain with an enlarged abdominal aorta. On 18th April, at 1:15 a.m., muttering in German, he died. No one was in attendance except a nurse, who spoke no German. No one recorded the last words of this extraordinary representative of a 'people who, ever since Abraham came out of Ur to mark the turn to monotheism, have fertilized civilization with ideas, from Moses and Jesus to Marx, Freud and Einstein.'[5]

CHAPTER TWO

The Age of Uncertainty

The unruly waters of a mountain torrent, the foam of a breaking wave, scudding storm-driven clouds, the patter of raindrops on a roof are variations on a single theme — a motif of disorderly, unpredictable natural forces exercised without regard for our ability to itemize, calculate or control. Embodiments of randomness and chaos, they refute the old-fashioned picture of a fully predictable, deterministic universe. We can never predict where the raindrop will fall or when the foam bubble will burst; nor can we foretell the precise shape of the cloud ten minutes hence. Intuition always whispered as much. Now science confirms it: no physics, no mathematics, no miracle of modern computing will ever achieve such detail. We now know, beyond much doubt, that our world is, in some ways, *intrinsically* unpredictable.

Like all life on Earth, society is imbedded in the physical environment. If this is indeterministic, so then are our correlative biological and social systems. One must expect, however, that the behaviour of society as a whole will be even less predictable than that of a relatively 'simple' environmental system such as the atmosphere — not only because the whole is more complex than its parts, but because it is no longer an inert system governed solely by physical laws. It contains humans (and other life forms) with consciousness, free will and the power to interact capriciously with their environment. Nevertheless, to have a sensibly operating society, we must be able to plan. The nature and scale of such plans are still open to endless, and largely ideological, debate. But to plan on *any* scale we must have forecasts. This requires a measure of predictability. Recent developments in physics and applied mathematics have interesting things to say about this problem.

19

It had been believed, until recently, that all social, economic and political predictions are unreliable for two main reasons: ignorance of how our complex economic/social/environmental systems work, and the intrinsic cussedness i.e., free will of human beings. Even E.F. Schumacher, an economist with fine credentials as a sceptic, once wrote that, were it not for ignorance and free will, the world would be fully predictable.[1] Today, such views are no longer tenable: we now know that even a universe devoid of human intervention would be intrinsically unpredictable. To digest this statement, it may help to put it into historical context.

Awareness that the universe is neither deterministic nor fully causal has come slowly. It is, in a sense, the antithesis of the scientific optimism of the Enlightenment, a state of mind which traced its roots to Newton and saw the universe as mechanism, a giant piece of clockwork running with smooth accuracy in accordance with the laws of Newtonian, or *classical*, mechanics. In this world the motion of the planets was predictable with a precision limited only by the inaccuracies of our measuring instruments; there seemed every reason to believe that this held true for all forms of matter. In this fully deterministic model, all effects had definite causes, ascribable to known laws. During the eighteenth century, and through most of the nineteenth, this was the message of science. In his *Critique of Pure Reason* (1781), Kant's Second Analogy of Experience stated that 'All changes take place according to the law of connection between cause and effect'.[2] In 1812 the great French mathematician Laplace made his famous assertion about the Divine Calculator who, given the exact positions and velocities of all particles of matter at one instant, would be able to predict the future with complete accuracy and for all time. The world was fully accessible to reason and, given a thorough knowledge of its workings and sufficient data, we would some day have almost unlimited powers for reshaping it — in any way we wished.

The deterministic clockwork model began to crumble in the last decades of the nineteenth century. An important blow was the birth of the Maxwell-Boltzmann theory of gases — a new *statistical* mechanics. The premise here is that the number of particles — molecules or atoms — in even a thimbleful of gas is so huge that we can only describe their average behaviour: one has to resort to statistics. Deterministic laws still govern the motion of each particle, but there are far too many of these to allow one to calculate their individual motions (even the fastest conceivable computer would need running times exceeding the age of the universe). This model proved very successful, allowing physicists to explain the macroscopic (bulk) properties of gases. It also marked the explicit introduction of indeterminism into the foundations of physics. This however was merely a consequence of our not being able to carry out so many calculations at once. It did not so much reflect a property of Nature as an intrinsic human limitation. A Divine Calculator might still be up to His job.

Indeterminism scored a more important victory at the beginning of this century with the advent of *quantum* mechanics. Following the early breakthroughs of Planck, Einstein, Bohr and many others, this theory quickly established itself as the most accurate description of the world of molecules, atoms and nuclear particles — the basic building blocks of matter. It demonstrated that, on this microcosmic scale, classical mechanics did not work. Heisenberg's uncertainty principle stated that we cannot, at the same time, know both the position and the velocity of a small particle, because the act of measuring one of these quantities disturbed the other in unpredictable ways: the information required by the Divine Calculator was unavailable as a matter of principle. The new theory reduced matter to an interplay of probability waves in abstract spaces, and the radioactive disintegration of an atomic nucleus was shown to be entirely unpredictable — an event without a cause. Laplace and Kant had both been wrong: determinism had been an intellectual convenience, an act of faith which did not tally with the world of the atom. The universe was not entirely predictable.

Yet this was unpredictability *writ small*, for it concerned only the microcosm. Indeed, quantum theory itself could show that if one looked at large numbers of atoms — matter in bulk — classical mechanics was reinstated and still governed the macroscopic world with almost complete precision. The indeterminism of quantum theory was a remove away from our everyday world of global physics, weather, engineering, technology or economics. The paths of the planets, the flow of fluids, the Earth's air, oceans and rocks were still governed by classical physics. Because of Newton's laws aeroplanes flew, rockets took people to the moon, and most of our industrial machinery worked with satisfying accuracy. Well into this century it could be maintained that, whereas many events in our environment might seem random, this was but a reflection of our ignorance: better science, faster computers, more money for research would, it was felt, do away with such untidiness — after all, the laws of classical physics *were* deterministic. But applied mathematicians had long been aware of difficulties relating to the predictability of turbulent flows. By the early 1960s, thanks in part to better computers, it became established that such flows were in some respects truly unpredictable and illustrated a type of behaviour new to physics. By the late 1970s and early 1980s it had become obvious that such phenomena spanned many fields of science and they received a name: deterministic chaos or simply *chaos*. This introduced a new kind of 'indeterminism' into the environment — into the Newtonian, classical workaday world of our perceptions, technology, weather, economy and everyday lives. This was unpredictability *writ large*.

The rapid growth of physics following the Enlightenment and, well into this century, took place in part because the mathematical models — the equations — used to model the world had been relatively simple. They were what mathematicians call *linear*. In its simplest form linearity implies proportionality. A textbook example is that of a small weight hanging at the end of a spring; it stretches the spring by a certain amount, and a weight twice as large gives an extension twice as big, and so forth. Take the weight off, and the spring bounces back to its original size — all this is the principle of the spring balance. But putting a large weight on the spring gives quite different results: the spring may be permanently deformed (damaged) or even ruptured — its response is now *non-linear*. For small weights, the linear model describes the behaviour of the balance quite accurately. For many natural phenomena linear models make good enough approximations and, until recently, much of physical theory had used linear equations — either because the phenomena were intrinsically linear (electromagnetic waves, quantum theory) or because one limited oneself to small effects, as in the example of the spring balance. Progress had been correspondingly fast. But applied mathematicians, geophysicists, meteorologists and astrophysicists, knew very well that much of the real world does not behave in this simple way. Linear theory was merely an approximation — it only scratched the surface of things. However, the mathematics of non-linear systems can be woefully difficult and progress in this direction remained slow until the advent of modern computers in the late 1950s. We have since witnessed an explosion of new insights, amongst which has been the proof that most natural systems (physical, biological, geophysical) exhibit chaotic behaviour.

Chaos is a complex and subtle business. For the physicist it implies behaviour which, although unpredictable in some respects, also exhibits definite and sometimes predictable phenomena. In practice, the onset of chaos is clear: flow becomes turbulent when water runs too fast in too narrow a channel, waves break when they grow too large, eddies form and the drag on an airfoil increases suddenly at some critical speed. These phenomena all involve instabilities: the fast flow of water, the cresting wave, the stream of air around the airfoil become unstable. At some moment then, in some region of space, the system passes into a different mode — a new regime — and the complexion of things changes radically. Mathematical modelling shows that these transitions may be triggered by factors so tiny as to be untraceable — by what mathematicians call infinitesimal perturbations. This is why they can be intrinsically unpredictable. The macroscopic laws of classical physics governing the motion are deterministic; the distribution of minute perturbations is not. Since new regimes may themselves prove unstable, a system can develop complicated superpositions of motions of all scales: the result may be the kind of turmoil seen, for instance, in a mountain torrent. An important feature of this form of chaos is that, as long as we confine our attention to a definite regime or scale (a particular slice of time and space) some aspects of the system *are* predictable: an eddy carried along by the flow maintains its identity for a while, a wind-driven cloud may keep its shape for some minutes. The physics within such units is reasonably predictable (this is what makes weather forecasting feasible). Only the transitions — appearance or disappearance of vortices, changes in regime — may be capricious.

A computer model, of course, mirrors nature and will also display this type of chaotic behaviour. In modelling systems like the atmosphere (weather forecasting), minute differences in the data fed into the computer may lead to startlingly different results. This implies that observational (measurement) inaccuracies may generate a form of mathematical chaos like that seen in nature: detailed forecasts beyond a certain limit are impossible.

This conception of chaos developed in the 1950s and 1960s, in studies of the theory of weather forecasting, although its adumbration can be traced to earlier theories of turbulence or to purely mathematical insights (Poincaré, 1891).[3] The operative physical laws here are deterministic: the equations of fluid flow merely express classical Newtonian laws, but they are, for a continuous material, non-linear. This allows for a bewildering variety of unstable activity which is still being unravelled. E.N. Lorenz's pioneering studies at MIT in the 1960s[4] showed this very clearly, demonstrating that even the most powerful and modern computers cannot give reliable and detailed weather forecasts for more than one or two weeks ahead. Yet in all this complexity there is order of a sort — islands of temporary stability within an enormously complicated sea of possible behaviours to which the system is attracted. Such islands correspond to what mathematicians, studying the problem in abstract spaces, have called *strange attractors*.[5,6]

The Earth's atmosphere may be taken as a prototype for natural chaotic systems. It clearly illustrates the properties of chaos and the problems facing the forecaster. In particular, it demonstrates the need for defining scales in space (e.g., local *vs.* global) and time (short term *vs.* long term), as well as the quality (detail) expected of a forecast. Thanks to satellites and modern computers meteorology now has a good understanding of these factors — of the limitations of its forecasts and, generally, of atmospheric patterns of activity.

Global weather systems consist, normally, of wave-like successions of high and low pressure cells (Rossby waves). These are usually carried along, at speeds close to a thousand

kilometres a day, by fairly steady westerly air streams — giant
vortices, essentially, with widths of several thousand kilometres
and lifespans of the order of days or weeks. Evanescent islands
of stability, they tend to move from west to east across the
surface of the globe, splitting or coalescing, disappearing
and reforming, like eddies on the surface of some great,
fast-flowing river. Eddies are, in fact, characteristic modes
of motion of the atmosphere: dust devils, waterspouts, torna-
does, thunderstorms, hurricanes are examples on other scales.
When one such appears it can be followed for a while, its evolution understood and charted. But their distribution in time
and space, their appearances and disappearances are largely
unpredictable.

Medium range regional forecasts — of the kind seen on TV
or in the papers — are governed chiefly by the Rossby wave
motion of the highs and lows. They allow one to predict
winds, temperatures, precipitation and cloud cover for land
areas of a few thousand square miles, with better than 80 per
cent accuracy for periods of twenty-four to forty-eight hours.
Predictions of similar detail and accuracy for a whole week
are more chancy, but possible in principle. At longer periods
their quality deteriorates rapidly; chaos precludes such forecasts for more than a week or two. More modest forecasting
goals, limited to regional averages, allow one to extend one's
predictions to longer time-spans and larger, global scales —
although chaos is also encountered here. Thus seasonal average temperatures are fairly stable, and regional climates conform to well-established patterns. But we cannot foretell many
truly important long-term effects — such as the magnitude of
the global warming due to the greenhouse effect (CO_2 and
methane pollution), or the timing and nature of any sudden
transitions which may go with it. Paleoclimatic studies suggest the existence of instabilities on the longer time-scales of
centuries or millennia.[7]

Scientists of another generation would have guessed that
our ability to predict the detailed behaviour of simple non-
linear systems like fluids, or even the weather, was indefinitely
perfectible: better data, more knowledge would always lead to
more detailed and accurate predictions. This, we now know,
was an illusion. Unpredictably, a small cloud may grow into

a thunderhead, an air vortex gestating quietly off the coast of Africa may suddenly pick up strength, start moving and turn into a hurricane, or a freak tornado may drop its dark funnel earthward and cut a swathe of devastation through some Mid-western town or city. The precise location and timing of such events will not be found in our weekly, or even daily, predictions. Their very possibility may, on the day, escape the forecaster, for their triggers can be minute, subtle and untraceable. As one eminent meteorologist once put it, the flap of a seagull's wing could affect next month's weather.

The atmosphere and oceans, the planet's ecology, the global economy, our whole society are huge, interrelated, unstable systems. The world we live in is akin to a great river, a turbulent collection of eddies carried along by the currents of time — vanishing and reappearing, growing, interacting, coalescing. Each eddy — a localized, temporary island of stability, a region of relatively organized and steady behaviour — is due for destruction at some unknown time and place, often by unknown causes. Like Heraclitus' river, this world is never the same; it is erratic and unpredictable. Our Western Cartesian faith in a reasonable universe remains, but modern science is demonstrating its limitations — it is telling us to be more modest. Predictions and forecasts are possible, but not on all scales and not at all times.

There is little doubt that the theory of chaos stands for a radical shift in our view of the universe. It is, in the full sense of the word, a scientific revolution. But its practical implications have yet to be assessed, particularly in their consequences for society. Since the concept of chaos applies to our everyday environment it is, inevitably, relevant to our local, national and global affairs. It suggests explicitly that society must function in unstable, chaotic and intrinsically unpredictable ways — a view corroborated by even the most schematic outline of history. Most, maybe all, of humanity's great blueprints for action and many of its outstanding ideas and insights have led to results that were neither foreseen nor desired by their initiators. Marx never dreamt that his theories would be first put to use in industrially backward Russia, nor did he foresee the repressive society that resulted. Neither Christ nor his early followers would have conceived, let alone approved, the

murderous excesses of the crusades or the Spanish Inquisition. In 1905 neither Einstein, nor anyone, would have guessed
that, a bare forty years later, $E=mc^2$ would lead to the mass
slaughters of Hiroshima and Nagasaki. Recent history offers
an endless list of political and technical undertakings, from
peace treaties to medicines, which have gone awry and led to
disaster. It is difficult, at this superficial, preliminary stage of
our understanding, to separate irreducible uncertainties from
the more familiar effects of bad judgment or stupidity —
themselves, perhaps, part of the system's chaos (Chernobyl).
However, mathematical study of far simpler subsystems like
the atmosphere conveys the clear message that, even were we
to know all that can be known about the workings of society, its
evolution would still be essentially unpredictable. Just as, at the
turn of the century, physicists had to accept the indeterministic nature of their laboratory universe, just so we must swallow
the fact that chaos is part of the very fibre of society. We never
know what *strange attractor* may take over our destiny.

The knowledge that the structure of our socio-economic
world is intrinsically chaotic is not particularly helpful. By
itself it suggests only that we cannot do much better than
we are — that we should carry on as before. It might even
be seen as endorsing the Kafkaesque sort of inactivity we
so often witness in our giant bureaucracies. However, in
its analysis of the actual properties of chaos, the theory is
more instructive. Specifically, it proffers the advice that there
are, in chaotic systems, scales and modes of activity that
are predictable: these tell us what kind of forecasts can be
made. Weather forecasters do make useful predictions, albeit
for limited spans of space and time. In the social context we
should be able to emulate them by trying to define plausible
scales of social and economic forecasting — the relevant space
and time constraints on planning. Human groupings do occur
in hierarchies — families, villages, towns, countries, alliances.
We know, too, that within these scales planning takes place,
sometimes successfully. However, we can neither tell if these
are optimum scales, nor how accurately we can ever hope to
plan. We have no way, yet, of defining the real constraints
— but we know they exist. Whatever their ideologies, faiths
or goals, men and women have, through all of history, ruled

or governed without understanding the limits of government — with no real knowledge of the constraints under which they were operating. The theory of chaos states not only that such limits exist, but that it will be worth our while to identify them.

People have always lived in groups. Whatever they first sought to accomplish thereby — safety from nature's unpredictable forces, from predators or from their fellow humans — matters little now. The point is that, as communities grew and multiplied, as nature's capriciousness became less menacing, new kinds of problems appeared — problems of group interaction, communal discord and competing interests. History is, in part, the record of our often less than successful efforts to deal with this increasingly chaotic social environment. Through the centuries and millennia philosophers and economists have generated many theories, a kind of shopping list of suggestions for coping with this social turmoil. All were basic recipes for replacing chaos with order and simplicity. Leaving aside the vast field of other-worldly, religious solutions, they fell into two groups: straight utopias (Plato, Francis Bacon) and economic models (Marx, Adam Smith).* Both categories appear to have suffered from at least two fatal flaws: they had no conception of the real complexity and chaos of human society, and they were based on crude caricatures of human psychology. Discounting the miserable experience of fascism, the utopias have not really been tried — fortunately, perhaps. The economic theories *have* been applied — without notable success. They have led either to repressive Marxist states or to the economic and political sophistries of capitalism. Elsewhere, it looks as if mixtures of ideological, economic and religious arguments have been used to rationalize the interests of autocrats, empire-builders, industrialists, merchants and, more recently, big corporations. The end result — the modern world — is a patchwork of states whose boundaries are the result of power struggles recent and ancient, of wars, treaties and compromises whose purpose is often long forgotten and having little to do with the needs or even the cultural affinities

---

* Admittedly it may be difficult to draw the line. Economic theories, and Marxism in particular, may have a strong utopian streak.

of the people. The world's largest state, the Soviet Union, offers us the spectacle of a highly centralized government running an amalgamation of more than a hundred different 'nationalities' with different cultures, languages and religions. The assumption that one could make forecasts and plans for such a motley collection was always implausible; almost seven decades of repression made the point. The governments of many other modern countries are analogous to that of the Soviet Union in at least one respect: rationalized by *a priori* ideologies, they are efforts to force order out of chaos — with little regard to the human cost.

It is probably no coincidence that the best run states tend to be small and culturally homogeneous: the Netherlands, Denmark, Norway and Sweden have little or no poverty, fine social security systems, high-quality medical care, better than average civil rights records and a tolerance of political diversity. By comparison, the great economic and political giants have, to put it politely, erratic records. Thus the Soviet Union and the USA, with contrasting forms of government, both rely on centralized planning; both have culturally inhomogeneous populations. The Soviet Union's record of political and religious repression, from the 1920s until quite recently, illustrates a traditional method of coping with unpredictability: the use of tyranny to impose uniformity and, thus, predictable behaviour. The USA, with its more libertarian philosophy, has eschewed this solution. It has put its faith in market forces to guide a highly centralized federal government. This kind of *laissez faire* is currently yielding a million hungry, homeless street people and astonishing levels of political corruption. Other behemoths, like India or China, could have served equally well as object lessons on the danger of coupling centralization with bigness and cultural diversity. In tyrannies or democracies, centralized planning of large socio-economic units has a poor record.

Perhaps small *is* beautiful. Unfortunately, in the social context, we do not know, yet, how to be more precise — unlike the meteorologist who understands full well on what scales, and with how much detail, she/he operates. Within our social scene there are hints, no more. In the weather's daily chaos are islands of relative stability, within which we can practice our forecasting skills. Within the world's social systems we glimpse only outlines — families, towns, countries small and large; we have yet to identify and carefully map our islands, truly to define the limits of planning and government. How, when or if we shall achieve insight of this order is uncertain. Society interacts with its environment but is not, for all that, a physical phenomenon; much of it is *mind* and it functions in more subtle and far more complex ways than any purely physical system. How much so is perceived by skimming generalist weeklies like *Nature* or *Science*: information is cascading upon us from all sides — ethology, ecology, biology, psychology, earth and environmental sciences, anthropology, economics are swamping us with new and one trusts relevant information. Just what an eventual synthesis of all this will tell us about ourselves and our society, no one can tell. Out of all this travail, new forms of order will doubtless emerge. Someday, it has been suggested, we may decide that society is, effectively, a super-organism — like a beehive, or an anthill of the mind. Perhaps. It is early days. One thing though is clear: while we shall always make plans, a degree of chaos and anarchy is ineradicable and natural. A fully causal, predictable (calculable) model of society is a mirage which has, already, done us harm enough — it is no more conceivable than an accurate weather forecast extending into an indefinite future. If, as has been said, wisdom is the acceptance of the inevitable then, on some level, we must learn to live with anarchy.

At best, then, all long-term prognoses, any kind of futurology are suspect. But the great environmental debates of the past decades have been crippled by the inability of most of us, and of our technocrats in particular, to come to terms with this fact. The world we live in — our environment — is a complex non-linear system; chaotic and unpredictable, it turns all our arguments into conflations of fact and faith. This tends to make rational discussion of issues extremely difficult.

A classic example of this kind of debate concerns the future of nuclear power. The complexities are endless; economic, ecological, environmental, social, political, geological questions, and many others, are involved — all embroil one, willy-nilly, with indeterministic and unquantifiable phenomena. The pollution problems alone are arresting: one must be concerned, into the decades and centuries ahead, with the steady diffusion into the environment of small amounts of radioactive discharge — the long-term effects of which are unknown. Equally serious are the difficulties of disposing of old plants or spent fuel. For present purposes, let us focus on the latter, i.e., on the so-called high-level waste disposal problem. Assume, for the sake of argument, the case of a nuclear economy supplying ten per cent of the world's electricity from water-cooled reactors similar to those currently in use. It would generate yearly waste radioactivity equivalent to thousands of tons of pure radium — coming in a broad assortment of chemical species, with half-lives varying from a few decades to hundreds of thousands of years. Current long-term plans involve disposing of this waste, in some relatively insoluble solid form, in the seabed or in rock formations on land. The practicalities of such disposal confront us directly with our inability to make reliable predictions concerning the effects of the earth's seismicity, underground water flows, ocean currents, the climate. Yet proponents of nuclear power have often maintained that they can guarantee confinement in geological formations on land or in the ocean bed for thousands or even millions of years. This is an act of faith, albeit defended by scientific arguments relating to solubility of wastes, integrity of the site, leaching, and so forth. The opposite opinion — that containment will, sooner or later, fail — is also held on faith, and bolstered by a different, equally convincing, set of facts. Neither view is demonstrably true. But the theory of non-linear systems shows that our environment and our technological enterprises are chaotic and unpredictable, that small perturbations thereof often lead to unexpected and disproportionately large effects. This suggests that opponents of geological waste disposal have the stronger case — be it only because, in cases involving great potential dangers, it makes better sense to err on the side of caution. 'Prudence,' said Epicurus 'is a more precious thing even than philosophy.'[8]

Circumspection of this kind would seem advisable in all our technological endeavours. Not only the mathematics of chaos, but technocracy's track record itself demonstrate the impossibility of predicting or controlling the effects of technology — there have simply been too many catastrophes, too many wrong turns. Leaving aside the unsuccessful gropings of economists and of our statesmen/women, we have had thalidomide, Soweso, DDT, industrial explosions, collapsing dams, worldwide pollution, Chernobyl, disappearing ozone, the greenhouse effect . . . an appalling list. The public, aware of vast threats lurking in the background, is worried and uncertain. Less innocent than in the past, it is no longer convinced by the stage entrances of learned men and women, brandishing diplomas and assuring us that all is well, because they understand the problem, even if we do not. Besides, for every expert saying that things are under control, there is another to contradict him, and the listener may have to consider the various experts' politics, sources of funds, or other sources of prejudice. This need not be an aspersion upon any of the experts' honesty so much as a reflection on the fact that, in advising us on the consequences of some action involving chaotic or potentially chaotic systems, he or she will have to make judgments on a basis of faith. This, clearly, opens the door to subjective factors — conscious and unconscious ones. Chaos, in other words, does more than curtail our power: it affects the essence of the advisory processes in our society. Expert advice can no longer be seen as reflecting purely technical, quantitative arguments — it has, inevitably, lost a measure of objectivity, even when issuing from honest men and women. It has, of course, ever been true that our important social decisions, just like our private personal ones, had, to some degree, been acts of faith. The theory of chaos tells us that this will always be so, that it is wrong and dangerous to pretend that, somehow, someday, modern technology and science will change this, — totally replacing, as it were, faith by knowledge. This can never be true. Science itself is teaching us the limits of our power.

CHAPTER THREE

Of Science and Method

MAÎTRE DE PHILOSOPHIE: '. . . all that is not prose is verse: and all that is not verse is prose'.
JOURDAIN: 'And the way one talks, what is that?'.
MAÎTRE DE PHILOSOPHIE: 'That is prose'.
JOURDAIN: 'Forsooth! Here it is more than forty years that I have been talking prose without ever knowing it, and I am most grateful to you for having taught me that'.

(Molière, *Le Bourgeois Gentilhomme*, II-4)

Confronted by the philosophy of science, the practising scientist feels a bit like Monsieur Jourdain. To have one's common-sense and professional habits dissected in a search for rules and method can be surprising, even unnerving. Yet the experience may be salutary for, unlike Molière's Mâitre de Philosophie, the philosophers of science have said much that is genuinely illuminating. For more than two thousand years — since Aristotle — they have tried, with various degrees of success, to understand and tell us how science works — seeking *the* method, the secret of its success, the philosopher's stone.

Of late, philosophers have been more modest, and no doubt wiser. Many have concluded, more or less, that logical exegesis is wasted and that there is no scientific method. As Peter Medawar once noted, had there been one — a set of recipes for making reliable discoveries — any scientist working in an institution devoted to finding the causes of some as yet incurable disease should be dismissed for, clearly, he/she is either incompetent or too lazy to apply it. The most promising approach for understanding how science works, philosophers now advise us, is historical and social. Go back to the sources, says Feyerabend; develop a palaeontology of ideas and treat these in evolutionary terms says Toulmin; look at science as the history of wars of attrition between competing research programmes, says Lakatos. And so on.

Scientists have not always been helpful to philosophers trying to clarify the workings of their craft. Einstein would not be pinned down:

> [the scientist] must appear to the systematic epistemologist as a type of unscrupulous opportunist: he appears as a realist insofar as he seeks to describe a world independent of the acts of perception; an idealist insofar as he looks upon the concepts and theories as free inventions of the human spirit (not logically derivable from what is empirically given); as positivist insofar as he considers his concepts and theories justified only to the extent to which they furnish a logical representation of relations among sensory experiences. He may even appear as Platonist or Pythagorean insofar as he considers the viewpoint of logical simplicity as an indispensable and effective tool of his research.[1]

James Clerk Maxwell, for all his nineteenth-century philosophical education, felt that the act of discovery was beyond analysis:

> I believe there is a department of the mind conducted independent of consciousness, where things are fermented and decocted, so that when they are run off they come clear.[2]

P.W. Bridgman, a physicist and philosopher, put his views succinctly:

> I like to say that there is no scientific method as such, but rather only the free and utmost use of intelligence . . .[3]

It was, I suppose, foreordained that sooner or later philosophers of science would also turn against the idea of method. Thus Ian Hacking:

> Why should there be *the* method of science? There is not just one way to build a house, or even to grow tomatoes. We should not expect something as motley as the growth of knowledge to be strapped to one methodology.[4]

Much of Paul Feyerabend's writing is devoted to the demolition of methodologies:

> ... there is no 'scientific method'; there is no single procedure
> or set of rules that underlies every piece of research and
> guarantees that it is 'scientific' and, therefore, trustworthy
> ... Scientists revise their standards, their procedures, their
> criteria of rationality as they move along and enter new domains
> of research just as they revise and perhaps entirely replace their
> theories and their instruments as they move along and enter
> new domains of research. The main argument for this answer
> is historical: there is not a single rule, however plausible and
> however firmly grounded in logic and general philosophy that
> is not violated at some time or other.[5]

I selected these quotes because they mirror important new
trends and suggest that we stop theorizing about logical structure, go back to the sources and try to make sense of how science works by looking at how things actually happened. From
this angle, the efforts of conventionalists, justificationists, logical reconstructionists, falsificationists, logical positivists, and
so on are becoming passé. This much, at least, is implied by
Feyerabend's well-known title: 'The Philosophy of Science: A
Subject with a Great Past'.[6]

A great past indeed, and an interesting one, which deserves
to be better known. Like so much else we can trace it to
ancient Greece, and to the pre-Socratics. Pythagoras, with
his conflation of reality and number, established a point of
view to which many a modern theoretical physicist will still
subscribe: number is the essence of things. One might claim,
says Sarton,

> that the physicists of all ages, the natural philosophers, have
> been constantly allured by the hope of finding new numerical
> relations. It is as if they had heard old Pythagoras whisper in
> their ears: The number is the thing.[7]

The Pythagoreans bequeathed us a faith and the makings of an
epistemology, but no method.

In the study of method Aristotle was far more important. He
has had immense and durable influence on the philosophy of
science. Unlike Pythagoras, and unlike his teacher Plato, he
was an empiricist: he saw science as going from observation
to general principles and back to observation. His methods

of deduction were primarily syllogistic and he insisted that, to obtain correct premisses, the investigator had to observe nature:

> Scientific knowledge through demonstration is impossible unless a man knows the primary immediate premisses . . . out of sense-perception comes to be what we call memory, and out of frequently repeated memories of the same thing develops experience; for a number of memories constitute a single experience. From experience again . . . originate the skill of the craftsman and the knowledge of the man of science, skill in the sphere of coming to be and science in the sphere of being.[8]

Science according to Aristotle deduces consequences from premisses obtained by observation. In contemporary language one would say that Aristotle's is an inductive-deductive model. Like all us lesser mortals, he did not always practise what he preached. Aristotelian mechanics would have been less awry — and had a less negative influence in future centuries — had the master deigned to observe more carefully an arrow's — or any object's — flight. Notably missing in Aristotle's method is experimentation, as distinct from observation — the interventionary ingredient so vital to the eventual flowering of Western science. An important flaw, to be sure; but one must not underrate Aristotle's enormous contribution: to borrow Feyerabend's phrase, Aristotle is not a dead dog.

Stressed by Aristotle, and important for science and philosophy, is the logical distinction between *necessary* and *contingent* truths. This is illustrated by phrases such as 'All men are mammals' or 'All ravens are black'. The first brooks no exceptions: it is a necessary truth. But it is conceivable that, someday, someone will discover a white raven: the second statement, then, is a merely contingent truth. Aristotle believed that scientific truths were necessary ones — a point of view abandoned after Locke and Newton, or possibly before.

With the demise of Hellenistic culture, Aristotle's influence waned. From the fourth century on, the natural philosophy of Western Christendom had little to do with empiricism. It was largely Platonic, i.e., idealistic and dualistic. The world

of ideas was seen as real and perfect, and the world of the
senses as an inferior copy thereof. Augustine was the spokesman for this philosophy, which ruled almost unquestioned for
seven hundred years.

In the twelfth century Robert Grosseteste, and then Thomas
Aquinas, using newly translated Arab and Byzantine manuscripts, expounded and interpreted Aristotle with great success. So much so that for the next four hundred years — from
about 1200 till 1600 — Aristotle was reborn, and his views held
sway in most of Europe. His induction-deduction method
became the base upon which Grosseteste and Roger Bacon
built — the latter augmenting it with the decisive, albeit in his
hands largely theoretical, concept of active experimentation.
Western science is thus the child of Aristotle. His occasional
bad press among historians of science is undeserved. It is
the doing of too many medieval academics, unimaginative
philosophers and theologians who used him as an authority
— i.e., as a stultifying, rather than a dynamic influence.

Early in the seventeenth century, Galileo brought this period
to an end, linking experiment and mathematics into their modern alliance; and he successfully put to flight the incompetent
Aristotelian academics of his day — with dire results for himself. He was one of the greatest scientists of all time, yet we look
in vain to him for enlightenment on the problem of method.
No paragon of careful, systematic methodology or even (some
say) of intellectual integrity, many of Galileo's experiments are
now believed to have been careless, his reasoning often suspect and sometimes wrong. He *was* the first modern physicist,
a man of powerful intuition, a towering unorthodox genius
but, popular myth notwithstanding, he left us no 'scientific
method'. Feyerabend, after a thorough study of Galileo's ways,
writes:

> Galileo *changes* his method whenever he thinks nature has
> changed its procedures, or whenever he runs into obstacles
> created by human psychology and physiology . . . Nor does he
> avoid rhetoric. He is one of the few scientists . . . who realizes
> that it is not enough to 'strive for truth', but that the way to the
> truth must be made *visible* for man and that purely logical pro-
> cedures must therefore be used side-by-side with *rhetoric*. Seen

from an empiricist point of view much of what Galileo does is deception; seen from a more enlightened point of view it shows a marvellous insight into the complexities of knowledge.[9]

Ian Hacking picks up and repeats the judgment when he says that Feyerabend has used the case of Galileo

> to urge that great science proceeds as much by propaganda as by reason: Galileo was a con man, not an experimental reasoner.[10]

Con man or not, Galileo was a genius — the first to assimilate in practice the interplay of theory and experiment.

Francis Bacon, Galileo's English contemporary, devoted *his* great talents to propagandizing and discussing the allurement of science. Today he is mostly admired as a propagandist. His ideology differs radically from those of Plato and Aristotle who, on the same side for once, took science as the pursuit of knowledge for its own sake. Bacon's emphasis was on the *power* of knowledge and, as he was at pains to specify, on the power it offers for alleviating the human condition — on what he called 'that knowledge whose dignity is maintained by works of utility and power'.

Like Galileo, he attacked the dogmatic Aristotelians of his day:

> The propositions now in use, having been suggested by a scanty . . . experience and a few particulars of most general occurrence, are made for the most part just large enough to fit and take these in . . . And if some opposite instance, not observed or known before, chance to come in the way, the proposition (instead of being abandoned as false) is rescued and preserved by some frivolous distinction.[11]

But, as an empiricist, he agreed with Aristotle that scientific knowledge comes through observation rather than by the exclusive use of reason:

> In order to penetrate into the inner and further recesses of nature it is necessary that (our) notions . . . be derived from things by a more sure and guarded way . . . We must lead men to the particulars themselves, and their series and order; while men on their side must force themselves for awhile to lay their notions by and begin to familiarize themselves with facts.[12]

Bacon made heroic efforts to establish *induction* as *the* method of empirical science. After detailing the main sources of error in the interpretation of observations, he gives, in his *Novum Organum*, examples of the method at work. This consists in selecting a phenomenon to be investigated (such as heat) and drawing up long lists of occurrences, absences and comparisons. It is totally impracticable — if only because it ignores the need for preliminary hypotheses in structuring the data. Actually one cannot even begin collecting the necessary facts without some hypothesis to eliminate the infinity of irrelevant sense data (thus, in the classic success story of induction applied to a mass of data — the formulation in 1869 of the periodic table of elements — Mendeleyev and Meyer had at their disposal preliminary hypotheses going back at least forty years!). Yet while Bacon's method was unworkable, his message was enduring and important: doing science is an *a posteriori*, not an *a priori* process.[13]

In France, René Descartes held very different views. He saw *deduction* as the proper road to knowledge (this, apparently, makes him a *rationalist*). He believed that if one started from ideas that were 'clear and distinct' (and therefore *true!*) one could not go awry — the great example from antiquity being, of course, Euclid's geometry. And so Descartes, in his *Discourse on Method*, beginning with his *Cogito ergo sum*, went on to prove the existence of God, of the World, of matter and so on. Using this peculiar procedure he 'deduced' Newton's first law of motion in the following form:

> Principle XXXVI. That God is the First Cause of movement and that He always preserves an equal amount of movement in the universe.
> Principle XXXVII. The First law of nature: that each thing as far as in it lies, continues always in the same state.
> Principle XXXIX. The second law of nature: that all motion is of itself in a straight line; and thus things which move in a circle always tend to recede from the centre of the circle that they describe.[14]

This must be a unique instance of a scientific law formulated, seemingly, from metaphysical principles (most likely Descartes knew beforehand the answer he wished to reach, perhaps from earlier sources).

During the Enlightenment the English saw Bacon as a great philosopher and maker of a revolution in scientific method, while the French, with equal fervour, promoted Descartes. Both have their rightful niche in the history of philosophy. But their views on scientific method are seen today as having been overly simplistic. The development of science has made use of, among other things, a mixture of induction and deduction. Newton, for example, combined the two and formulated his famous laws — which seemingly explained with perfect precision both the motion of planets and the mechanics of matter here on earth and changed the face of Western science.

Inspired in large measure by Newton's success, British philosophers like Locke (1632-1702) and Hume (1711-76) gave their critical attention to the workings of science. In particular, they focussed on the old Aristotelian distinction between necessary and contingent truths.

Locke was of the opinion that necessary truths about the physical world would be attained if its properties were to be precisely predicted from the behaviour of more basic entities, such as atoms — but he thought this forever beyond mankind's reach. The best that can be achieved in practice, he said, are inductive generalizations about associations and successions of phenomena.

Hume agreed with the last statement but denied that it was possible, even in principle, to attain necessary truths in our dealings with nature. He acknowledged that there can be intuitive premises, or truths of the mind (such as Euclid's axioms), from which one may deduce absolutely certain, i.e., *necessary* truths. These truths, however, are empty of physical content; *physical* truths dealing with the 'real' world are all *contingent*. Creative insight applied to sensory data — to physically observed facts — may lead to the formulation of successful and comprehensive theories like Newton's, but these do not achieve the status of necessary truth. It is not possible to attain this kind of truth from premises based on observation — simply because all observations are themselves only contingent truths.

Induction, in others words, does not lead to certified truth. Hume makes this clear in a famous statement:

That the sun will not rise tomorrow is no less intelligible a proposition, and implies no more contradiction than the affirmation, *that it will rise.* We should in vain, therefore, attempt to demonstrate its falsehood.[15]

In practical, commonsense terms, this is insane. As Bertrand Russell put it, it says that

The lunatic who believes that he is a poached egg is to be condemned solely on the ground that he is a minority.[16]

Hume's scepticism, nevertheless, appears logically unassailable.

Kant attempted to answer Hume by pointing out that, in cognition, one should distinguish between matter (content) and form. Hume's empirical knowledge, based on sense experience, is the matter, the *prima materia* of all cognition. According to Kant, the mind then provides the structure or *form* into which this material is organized. He supplied an elaborate description of forms, categories and principles of understanding which he believed to be characteristic of this organization. This systematic structuring of knowledge, he said, is intrinsic to the mind and is at least as important as Hume's inductive generalizations. It does not, however, circumvent Hume's scepticism concerning the empirical base of knowledge.[16] Furthermore, in the light of twentieth century physics, two of Kant's basic requirements for the possibility of objective knowledge — his *analogies of experience* — are not satisfied. These analogies are:

1. *The Principle of Permanence of Substance* (First Analogy). In all changes of phenomena the substance is permanent, and its quantum is neither increased nor diminished in nature.
2. *The Principle of Production* (Second Analogy). All changes take place according to the law of connection between cause and effect.
3. *The Principle of Community* (Third Analogy). All substances, so far as they can be perceived as coexistent in space, are always affecting each other reciprocally.[17]

The First Analogy is the conservation of matter. Unless we

interpret it in terms far broader than Kant intended, relativity theory makes it untenable. The Second Analogy is the principle of causality. Quantum theory has shown this to be false (effects such as radioactive disintegration take place without antecedent causes). Today Kant would have to admit that, on his own terms, objective empirical knowledge is impossible.

If then there be such a thing as *truth*, it is beyond our reach. Science has a merely probable validity, and our belief in causal connections is, as Locke and Hume have stated, only a matter of habitual expectation. Scientific inferences concerning the universe are always a gamble. They are justified not by logic, but by their success.

Truth therefore — *necessary* truth, at least — cannot be the secret of science's success. What is it then? This question has puzzled, and continues to puzzle, philosophers and philosophically-minded scientists alike. It has led to the emergence of a new intellectual industry: the philosophy of science.

Nineteenth-century philosophy of science (W. Whewell, J.S. Mill, John Herschel), in a painstaking attempt to rationalize what scientists were doing so successfully, devoted itself, largely, to salvaging induction — and its interplay with deduction — on purely logical grounds. No doubt these efforts cleaned away some cobwebs; but they accomplished nothing so final as pinning down a method. More interesting, in this respect, are the philosophers of our century, who have had to ponder on whether the scientific method exists at all. The answer seems to be *no*, there is no such thing. Whatever the conclusion of the debate, interesting new points of view have clarified the question.

Between the two world wars, under the name of *logical positivism*, there flourished a modern outgrowth of classical empiricism. The label of *positivism* was coined by Auguste Comte early in the nineteenth century to describe his rather fuzzy, optimistic, positive use of science in the 'solution' of sociological and historical problems. Comte is now mostly forgotten ('Who remembers poor old Comte, long-winded, stuffy and not a success in life' says Ian Hacking),[18] but the noun survives as *logical* positivism — which is, by contrast, a sharp, anti-realist, anti-causal, pro-observation philosophy. A group that came to be known as the Vienna Circle (Schlick, Neurath, Carnap, Gode? and some satellite philosophers like A.J. Ayer) tried to reorganize philosophy, and to some extent language itself, by saying that any statement about the world which was neither empirically testable nor couched in the language of logic or mathematics had to be nonsense. In so doing, they hoped to draw a hard line between science and metaphysics — and, one is tempted to think, carry Hume to his logical conclusion.

Just as Locke and Hume had been inspired by Newton, so the Vienna Circle had been impressed by the successes of relativity and quantum mechanics, both of which suggested that unmeasurable or unobservable quantities in science be done away with. Relativity, for instance, had eliminated simultaneity and-or absolute space and time, and quantum theory had shown that the properties of 'things' depended on how they were measured. For twenty years or so — a whole generation — the Vienna Circle dominated European philosophy. Today it is accepted that there were serious defects in their ideology.

First of all, logical positivism is not internally consistent. Its basic premise — that all statements must be either empirically testable or stated in mathematical form — is no more than an act of faith: it is itself a non-testable, non-mathematical assertion.

There is, furthermore, no sharp boundary between observables and unobservables: history offers many examples of things not observable in one generation becoming eminently so in the next — molecules, genes, for example. And one no longer has faith in any unambiguous division between theory and observation: all observations are, to some extent, theory-laden. The old-fashioned sharp distinction between theory and observation has been historically useful for sorting out important issues — no one denies this. But today's scientists, with their incredibly sophisticated arsenal of instruments for 'seeing' and quantifying a myriad phenomena, know well that every measurement, every observation entails important theoretical assumptions about how both nature and their instruments work. Even the most basic cognitive development, to which Feyerabend likens the acquisition of scientific knowledge, is not 'theory-free' — it cannot proceed without some concurrently acquired theoretical foundation:

> . . . learning does not go from observation to theory but always involves both elements. Experience arises *together* with theoretical assumptions *not* before them, and an experience without theory is just as incomprehensible as is (allegedly) a theory without experience: eliminate part of the theoretical knowledge of a sensing subject and you have a person who is completely disoriented and incapable of carrying out the simplest action . . . All these discoveries cry out for a new terminology that no longer separates what is so intimately connected in the development of the individual and of science at large.[19]

Many contemporary philosophers hold similar views (Shapere, Hacking). They point out that the very language of modern particle physicists and astrophysicists makes the point: it is replete with imagery conflating theory and observation. They talk of 'observing' and 'seeing' quarks, of using neutrinos for 'directly observing' hot stellar cores, and so on.

Logical positivism, it seems, has had its day. So now, as Ian Hacking puts it:

> The usual Oedipal reaction has set in. Despite the impact of logical positivism on English-speaking philosophy, no one today wants to be called a positivist. Even logical positivists came to favour the label 'logical empiricist'. In Germany and France 'positivism' is, in many circles, a term of opprobrium, denoting an obsession with natural science and a dismissal of alternative routes to understanding in the social sciences.[20]

In the past few decades the philosophy of science has been dominated by a few names, amongst whom are Karl Popper, Imre Lakatos, T.S. Kuhn, S. Toulmin and Paul Feyerabend.

In the years immediately following the Second World War, Karl Popper was regarded by many as the dean of science philosophers. He was the great *falsificationist* — by virtue of his criterion for dividing science from non-science. The rules of empirical method, says Popper,

> must be designed in such a way that they do not protect any statement in science against falsification[21]

This was to be the demarcation line.

In a Popperian world, which held only ideal falsifiable scientific theories, the criterion itself would be unfalsifiable (there could be no possibility of counterexamples). So it is really a convention, or an edict — albeit a plausible one. In its bare *naive* form just quoted, Popper's criterion has trouble with the theory/observation dilemma: if all observations are theory-contaminated, how does one design an unbiased test? A modified form — so-called *sophisticated falsificationism* — partly circumvents the difficulty by introducing extra conditions. Such, for instance, is the requirement that there be, waiting in the wings, new theories, or *conjectures*, with greater powers of prediction. Eliminating a theory is then no longer a simple matter of destruction through falsification; there must be something better to replace it with.

Popper sees the history of science as an unending succession of false theories, a chain of conjecture — refutation — conjecture — etc., each successive conjecture in principle more powerful than the one before, yet still to be falsified some day. Characteristic is science's eternal susceptibility to revision: it is self-correcting. Better theories replace previous ones, with periods when competing theories overlap and vie for dominance.

Imre Lakatos focussed on this competition — which he saw as the norm. It being difficult to reduce the argument to one or two starkly defined conjectures or theories, he prefers to talk of *research programmes*. Lakatos has constructed an elaborate scheme describing the evolution, protection and replacement strategies of competing research programmes (recent examples of competing programmes have been: Newtonian *versus* Einsteinian gravitation, classical physics *versus* quantum mechanics, continental drift *versus* static models in geology). The rules of the game according to Lakatos are:

1. There is a *hard core* of knowledge which defenders of the programme take as inviolate (this assumption is called the *negative heuristic*). For instance, in the Newtonian celestial mechanics programme the inverse square law was the hard core. In the Einsteinian programme which

replaced it the hard core is the concept of curved space-time, i.e., Einstein's field equations.

2. There are techniques and methods for protecting, for as long as possible, the hard core from falsification (these form the *positive heuristic*). An example from the Newtonian programme was the practice of explaining all planetary orbit anomalies as perturbations due to forces exerted by other planets. The strategy worked well for two hundred years — it even led to the discovery of Neptune. It eventually failed in the case of Mercury: this was one of the factors which led to the replacement of the Newtonian programme by Einstein's.

Lakatos' picture is attractive because it is drawn from the history of real research programmes rather than, like most of its predecessors, from philosophical or logical imperatives. Like a number of contemporary philosophers, he felt those old-fashioned views to be arrogant:

Is it not then *hubris* to try to impose some *a priori* philosophy of science on the most advanced sciences? Is it not hubris to demand that if, say, Newtonian or Einsteinian science turns out to have violated Bacon's, Carnap's or Popper's *a priori* rules of the game, the business of science should be started anew?.[22]

According to Lakatos, then, it is history rather than philosophy that we should study. This, however, is also a chancy business: for different interpreters, identical historical observations may lead to quite contrary conclusions. So while others also take history as their guide, they come to quite different conclusions.

In the early 1960s T.S. Kuhn published *The Structure of Scientific Revolutions*. His (historical) thesis was that all major innovations have been rapid — more like crises, or revolutions, than the measured, reasoned changes of earlier philosophers. As older theories become inadequate, unable to cope with problems arising (like planetary orbit calculations), tensions are set up in the scientific community. These lead to a crisis, after which the world-view and the rules of the science change. Such *revolutions* are like *gestalt-shifts* — as in those drawings which can be seen either as a rabbit or as a duck: one's perception of a particular scene, of a particular set of facts is drastically and forever changed. Kuhn calls a particular viewpoint (rabbit, duck, inverse square law, curved space time) a *paradigm*. Between paradigm shifts are periods of calm, when *normal science* is done — this is the bulk of all scientific activity. It consists of *puzzle-solving*, i.e., of fitting the world systematically and patiently into the prevailing paradigm. Translated into the language of Lakatos, periods of normal science are times when given research programmes prevail. The reigning paradigm plays a role similar to Lakatos' hard core.

For Kuhn it is the puzzle-solving tradition of normal science, rather than the use of falsification tests that distinguishes science:

> . . . of the two criteria, testing and puzzle-solving, the latter is at once the less equivocal and the more fundamental.[23]

He uses astrology and medieval astronomy as examples:

> Compare the situations of the astronomer and the astrologer. If an astronomer's prediction failed and his calculations checked, he could hope to set the situation right. Perhaps the data were at fault: old observations could be re-examined and new measurements made, tasks which posed a host of calculational and instrumental puzzles. Or perhaps the theory needed adjustment, either by manipulations of epicycles, eccentrics, equants, etc., or by more fundamental reforms of astronomical technique. For more than a millennium these were the theoretical and mathematical puzzles around which, together with their instrumental counterparts, the astronomical research tradition was constituted. The astrologer, by contrast, has no such puzzles. The occurrence of failure could be explained, but particular failures did not give rise to research puzzles, for no man, no matter how skilled, could make use of them in a constructive attempt to revise the astrological tradition. There were too many possible sources of difficulty, most of them beyond the astrologer's knowledge, control, or responsibility. Individual failures were correspondingly uninformative, and they did not reflect on the competence of the prognosticator in the eyes of his professional compeers.[24]

(Similar reasoning may be used to rule out Marxist historiography or psychoanalysis as sciences.)

In *The Structure of Scientific Revolutions*, Kuhn points out that a revolutionary transition is not the outcome of a solely rational process:

> The man who embraces a new paradigm at an early stage must often do so in defiance of the evidence provided by problem-solving. He must, that is, have faith that the new paradigm will succeed with the many problems that confront it, knowing only that the older paradigm has failed with a few. A decision of that kind can only be made on faith.[25]

The adoption of a new paradigm by the scientific community, on the other hand, is analogous to a political revolution in that:

> Revolutions close with a total victory for one of the two opposing camps. Will that group ever say that the result of its victory has been something less than progress? That would be rather like admitting that they had been wrong and their opponents right. To them, at least, the outcome of revolution must be progress, and they are in an excellent position to make certain that future members of their community will see past history in the same way.[26]

Kuhn thus sees the practice and evolution of science as long periods of puzzle-solving (normal science), interrupted by spurts of revolutionary science (as in the birth of quantum mechanics or plate tectonics). But puzzle-solving is the ultimate criterion, the touchstone of true science. Not to put too fine a point on it, he is saying that original thinking is, for scientists, an abnormal activity.

Kuhn's model is a radical departure from its predecessors. Not surprisingly, it was attacked from numerous directions.

First, it was accused of inconsistency. Margaret Masterman[27] pointed out, somewhat acidly, that in his first book, Kuhn uses the word paradigm in at least twenty-one different senses. He has, apparently, eliminated some of this confusion in later versions.

Second, Feyerabend noted that Kuhn's definition of science can be applied with equal success to signal different enterprises. Since the essential ingredient of science is puzzle-solving, he does not see how we shall be able to exclude say, Oxford philosophy, or, to take an even more extreme example, *organized crime* from our considerations. For organized crime, so it would seem, is certainly puzzle-solving *par excellence*. Every statement which Kuhn makes about normal science remains true if we replace 'normal science' by 'organized crime'; and every statement he has written about the 'individual scientist' applies with equal force to, say, the individual safebreaker.[28]

Third, critics focussed on the concept of *revolution*. Lakatos accused Kuhn of irrationalism:

> For Kuhn scientific change — from one 'paradigm' to another — is a mystical conversion which is not and cannot be governed by rules of reason and which falls totally within the realms of the (social) *psychology of discovery*. Scientific change is a kind of religious change.[29]

Religious changes, like gestalt-switches, are, indeed, not rational processes; they are not susceptible to logical dissection. Yet they occur all the time — they are amongst the human psyche's characteristic modes of action. Irrational elements enter constructively in all fields of human endeavour — including science. The dynamics of creativity are still utterly mysterious, and the great men at the centre of science's revolutions have, more often than not, been incapable of explaining their breakthroughs in rational terms. We need only recall Einstein's mention that he was guided in his theoretical work by considerations of 'beauty', 'harmony', 'symmetry' and 'elegance', Kékulé's famous intuition into the ring structure of benzene after dreaming of a serpent swallowing its own tail, Maxwell's quasi-religious statements about his sources of inspiration ('what is done by what is called myself is, I feel, done by something greater than myself in me') . . .

Toulmin's view is that Kuhn's process of revolutionary change is at least exaggerated: paradigm shifts may be rapid, but they are not discontinuous. Toulmin has his own way of dealing with rapid change in science. He compares the evolution of scientific ideas with that of life forms through geologic time — a kind of Darwinian palaeontology of ideas in which only the fittest theories — paradigms — research programmes — survive. Toulmin asserts that Kuhn's concept of revolution relates to his model in the same way that Cuvier's catastrophism related to evolution. There *have* been periods of relatively rapid extinction, mutation and species-replacement — but this is all a matter of time-scale. Changes that looked sudden and catastrophic to Cuvier are now known to have been spread, in most cases, over thousands or even millions of years. One is also reminded of recent — and ongoing — wrangles over evolution between punctuationists and gradualists. Both are Darwinists, but punctuationists believe in periods of very rapid change (Kuhn's revolutions!) separated by periods of stagnation, with gradualists pushing for a slow succession of small step-by-step changes. As one reviewer has pointed out, Darwin would have been happy either way.[30] In Kuhnian revolutions, as in Darwinian evolution, there seems to be a degree of semantic confusion over such terms as gradual, sudden or revolutionary.

Paul Feyerabend also looks at history; his views differ as widely from those of Kuhn, Lakatos and Toulmin as they differ from each other. He argues forcibly that it is impossible to encase the workings of science in philosophical or historical strait-jackets. All cases are different. Like Toulmin he disputes the distinction between revolutionary and normal science and the existence of unique paradigms. There being no theory-independent observation language by which theories can be either justified or falsified with confidence, and no theory agreeing with *every* fact in its domain, Feyerabend sees all forms of logical reconstructionism, conventionalism, justificationism or falsificationism as suspect:

> Logicians cannot make sense of science — but they can make sense of logic so they stipulate that science must be presented in terms of their favourite logical system. This would be excellent comedy material were it not the case that by now almost everyone has started taking the logicians seriously.[31]

After a detailed analysis of Galileo's work, he has this to say:

> Galileo violates important rules of scientific method which were invented by Aristotle, improved by Grosseteste (among others), canonized by the logical positivists (such as Carnap

and Popper); contemporaries with very few exceptions over-looked fundamental difficulties that existed at the time; and modern science developed quickly, and in the 'right' direction (from the point of view of today's science lovers) because of this negligence. *Ignorance was bliss.* Conversely, a more determined application of the canons of scientific method, a more determined search for relevant facts, a more critical attitude, far from accelerating this development, would have brought it to a standstill.[32]

Feyerabend has been attacked on the grounds that he is an irrationalist, a polemicist and an anarchist. His wit, no doubt, has not endeared him to some of his fellow-philosophers (a chapter in one of his recent books[33] — a response to critics — is entitled 'From incompetent professionalism to professionalized incompetence — the rise of a new breed of intellectuals'! I commend it to all who consider entering a university career, in any field, as a fine lesson in the martial arts of academe). Yet Feyerabend is in many ways more modest than his predecessors, as in his answer to the question *What is Science?*:

> Every school in the philosophy of science gives a different account of what science is and how it works. In addition there are the accounts given by scientists, politicians and so-called spokesmen of the general public. We are not far from the truth when saying that the nature of science is still shrouded in darkness. Still, the matter is discussed and there is a chance some modest knowledge about science will some day arise.[34]

One of his most interesting ideas is an analogy between the workings of science and the learning processes of a child. As pedagogues have always told us, learning and play are closely linked. Feyerabend puts it this way:

> They (children) use words, they combine them, they play with them, until they grasp a meaning that has so far been beyond their reach. And the initial playful activity is an essential prerequisite of the final act of understanding. There is no reason why this mechanism should cease to function in the adult.[35]

Scientific research, Feyerabend is saying, is a kind of playful learning.

In a different context he remarks that

... philosophers of science who tried to understand and to tame science with the help of standards and methodologies that transcend research, *have failed*: one of the most important and influential institutions of our times is beyond the reach of reason as interpreted by most contemporary rationalists.[36]

Philosophers, clearly, are a contentious breed: from all these views there emerges no consensus. Yet the divergent philosophies of, say, Thomas Kuhn, Imre Lakatos, Ian Hacking and Paul Feyerabend, share one piece of common ground. Each argues, in his own way, that to make sense of the growth and workings of science we need the perspective of time; rather than dissect its logic, we would do well to ponder its history. This seems like good advice; but here too, apart from differences in opinion on what constitutes history, we encounter limits. Whatever else it may be, history is chaotic and the theory of chaos not only underlines the impossibility of long-term forecasts, it also precludes far-reaching and detailed retrodiction. Our universe, our world, our history are replete with effects whose ultimate causes we can never trace. If last week's flap of a seagull's wings may have determined today's weather, then a philosopher's sneeze may have, at some stage, influenced the course of science. And so, in reading the rest of this book, let my reader beware: *post hoc non propter hoc* — a chronological sequence is not a causal chain. Unless stated otherwise, an orderly description of events is not a deterministic picture of 'progress'. Whiggish conclusions will be the reader's, not mine.

CHAPTER FOUR

The Beginnings

In Europe and the British Isles there once flourished an ancient culture which, according to recent datings, anteceded the pyramids of Egypt. Whence these people came, and when, nobody knows. Neolithic builders of burial chambers, of stone circles and other peculiar structures, their monuments are everywhere — from the chill and misty islands of the North to the sunny shores of the Mediterranean. Curious stories, tales of human sacrifice and ancient magic surround these sites; but that is all they are: tales. This ancient culture had no writing and left no record other than its stones.

There is, about these structures, something oddly compelling. Maybe it is their antiquity; they are, after all, amongst our most ancient edifices — linking us palpably, across the millennia, to remote ancestors whose mode of life we have hardly begun to understand. Or perhaps it is their indestructibility; the more sophisticated structures of later civilizations are largely rubble, but the great henges, simple, sturdy collections of huge rocks, have survived with little sign of ravage. For more than four thousand years they have stood, or lain here, smoothed a little by rain, snow and wind, yet largely unscathed, recognizably here for a purpose, a message from the distant past.

Whoever they were, wherever they came from, these people were skillful builders; they made some of our most ancient buildings — houses perhaps five thousand years old which, with carefully constructed burial mounds, have been excavated in the Orkneys. Large stones went into their walls, heavy slabs extremely hard to move, yet so carefully dressed you cannot slip a knife blade between them. And they built huge monuments too, peculiarly elaborate arrays of rough-hewn boulders. Careful thought and much effort went into these; in Carnac they achieve a colossal scale, with a central megalith weighing 340 tons and stone alignments marching for miles across the countryside. Serious study suggests that they may have been used as astronomical observatories; from the great ring of Brodgar far north in the Orkneys to the menhirs of Carnac in Brittany, these prodigious monuments of bulky coarse-trimmed rock display delicately precise alignments with the sun and moon. At the very least, it has been said, they are the mute reminders of the skill, energy and determination of the engineers who built them. These strange works may have had astronomical or calendric purposes; perhaps they let their builders keep track of the ebb and flow of seasons.* Neolithic culture may have had at least the makings of a science.

But these ancient races left no written records; the first stirrings of science remain, largely, a matter for conjecture. The point has been made that language, myth, religion and science have common prehistoric roots. All are evidence of our propensity for symbol-making — of an abstract intelligence which led, inevitably, to the powerful concepts of number, mathematics and physics. The question of *when* this happened is almost meaningless. We know that the Chinese were toying with sexagesimal cycles in the thirtieth century BC and that Sumerian and Babylonian mathematicians and astronomers were already active around 2500 BC, measuring and creating a symbolic (and myth-laden) cosmos to describe their world of earth and sky.

Be it in the far North, or the Orient or in the Fertile Crescent of the Near East, the beginnings of science must have involved a measure of control over the environment; then, as today, knowledge had close links with technology and power. The domestication of animals, the appearance of agriculture, even the first stone tools were early intimations, the prerequisites of science as we know it. Crucial, in particular, was the transition to stable societies. When from food-gatherers, men and women became food-producers, the nomadic life gave way to

---

* Recent studies indicate that a Neolithic passage grave at Newgrange, Ireland, dating from about 3150 BC, may have been deliberately oriented to project a beam of sunlight on the central tomb wall, 18m from the entrance, at winter solstice. This would make it 'the oldest astronomically orientated structure in the world'.[1]

urbanization and to the development of property. With these came the need to count and to measure — essential ingredients of any science. All this had to do, on a variety of levels, with survival.

Other forces came into play when, in some sense, humanity ceased to be a species whose sole aim was to survive. Consider prehistoric paintings; certainly, they had magical purposes and this too was an effort at control — a search for power. Yet one day art became an activity in its own right, a discovery of form, a creative act satisfying some deep inherent need. And so it must have been with science; somewhere, sometime, perhaps with the Greeks, more likely before, pure science began. Understanding became an end in itself: it satisfied an elemental, uniquely human, psychic urge. We have, it seems, a need for meaning, for philosophy — for a metaphysics; it is, in C.G. Jung's sense of the word, a kind of basic religious drive. This must be, in part, how cosmologies arose, and how our abstract interest in nature came to be.

The early development of astronomy may also have had theocratic motives; a priesthood which could predict astronomical phenomena, from solstices to eclipses, would acquire power over the affairs of people. Whether Stonehenge and the great ring of Brodgar mirror a desire for knowledge or for power, we cannot tell; either way, they testify to an early intellectual activity which saw beyond the simple practicalities of day-by-day existence.

Beginning with stone tools, records of *technological* progress are more prevalent and ancient. But the use of metal for other than aesthetic purposes is relatively recent. Bronze metallurgy appeared in Sumer near the end of the fourth millennium BC; iron smelting arose in Armenia during the second millennium. Glassmaking was discovered by Egyptian craftsmen around 1600 BC.

The first firm records of mathematical and scientific achievement also come from the Middle East and the region of the Nile. In the fertile valleys of the Tigris and the Euphrates in Mesopotamia and of the Nile in Egypt humanity had, many millennia before Christ, settled down to a relatively stable and affluent agricultural life. Here, in contrast to other areas where stone-age farming soon exhausted the land, a cycle of floods renewed, yearly, the fertility of the soil. This allowed settled communities to arise — villages and towns. People acquired property, stored goods, raised herds. Writing, arithmetic, methods of measuring land and grain were born. In Sumer, simple arithmetic (with a positional notation, subsequently lost) was in use around 2500 BC. By then the Sumerians knew also how to calculate many areas and volumes. In the second millennium, under the Hammurabi dynasty, mathematics was further developed by the Babylonians. Their approach was practical; they did not generalize, preferring to express their results in terms of specific examples and concrete problems. Geometrical knowledge came from measuring: they discovered much of their mathematics as we did physics — inductively. In this way they found that, in a right-angle triangle, the square of the hypothenuse is equal to the sum of the squares of the other sides — what would one day be known as Pythagoras' theorem was, for them, an experimental fact. They were also able to solve systems of simultaneous quadratic equations as well as certain kinds of cubic ones. When we notice that such feats were accomplished without the benefit of modern algebraic methods, we understand that these early masters must have been the equals, in ability and talent, of today's finest mathematicians. These ancient Mesopotamian records come to us on broken clay tablets, scattered and fragmented by the stresses of time; our picture of Sumerian and Babylonian mathematics and science is very incomplete, but it seems that it is here that Western science has its roots.

The Egyptians, on the other hand, invented papyrus and Ahmose the scribe left the first systematic treatise on science to show us that in the valley of the Nile, too, a highly serviceable arithmetic had evolved at least four thousand years ago. There are two papyrus rolls: one in Moscow (the Golenischev papyrus), the other in the British Museum (the Rhind papyrus, transcribed by Ahmose). While slightly more recent, the latter is more systematic and informative; written in the seventeenth or eighteenth centuries BC they represent the knowledge of an earlier period (2000-1788 BC). The opening words of the Rhind papyrus — our most ancient scientific treatise — have a timeless quality which no modern scientist can fail to find moving:[2]

> Rules for enquiring into nature, and for knowing all that exists, every mystery . . . every secret. Behold this roll was written in the Year 33, month 4 of the inundation season . . . It was Ahmose the scribe who wrote this copy.

Eighty-four problems are stated and dealt with, starting with the use of fractions, and ending with the computation of areas and volumes — for most of which the ancient Egyptians had excellent approximations. Remarkably, they appear to have had a rigorous method for calculating the volume of the frustrum of a square pyramid.

For their astronomical work the Egyptians invented new sun-dials and instruments to measure the azimuth of stars, a fine solar calendar and tables of star culminations and risings. At the beginning of the second millennium the Babylonians made tables of the motion of Venus: at least as far back as the nine-teenth century BC people were scrutinizing the wandering of the planets across the heavens. They had by then discovered that Venus returns to the same point in the sky five times in eight years, and measured the period of Mercury as seen from earth to within five per cent (i.e., the *synodic* period which is about 116 days). They knew also that the moon, planets and sun stayed in approximately the same plane (the ecliptic). Observational astronomy, then, is at least four thousand years old.

Cosmological models, however, remained deeply rooted in myth. The early Babylonians saw the Earth and the heavens as two flat discs supported by water; later this was changed — the heavens became a hemispherical vault above which was more water, and above that the abode of the gods. The Egyptians, on the other hand, believed the universe to be a kind of box, the Earth being flat or slightly concave, with the heavens supported at four corners by mountain peaks. The Nile was, in this scheme of things, the offshoot of a universal river flowing around the world — all of which had little to do with the concurrent growth of astronomy and mathematics. These early scientists had observed and recorded the motion of the stars and planets, adding importantly to the fund of knowledge from which future ages would begin reinterpreting the universe. They had the intellectual capacity to make accurate observations: Pythagoras' theorem was for the Babylonians an experimental fact, the result of careful measurement; much of their mathematics was a practical response to the needs of commerce. But they never conceived a general experimental or observational approach to knowledge. Most of their sciences, such as medicine and chemistry, remained mixtures of hearsay and superstition, with illness ascribed to evil spirits and chemical rituals involving blood and embryos. The need for verifying their assertions by observation does not seem to have occurred to them.

Yet the beginnings of science in Babylon and Egypt had been tied intimately to the needs of everyday life, to practical objectives. Major errors in arithmetical procedure, or in computing areas, volumes or weights do not remain undetected for long in the pragmatic world of commerce — which, in effect, provides a continuous running check on the validity of methods used. In this way the pursuit of some forms of knowledge kept in touch with reality and prospered. This lesson, which seems so obvious to us now, was not to be fully digested for several thousand years. The Babylonians and Egyptians, certainly, proved strangely impervious to the idea that, as with the truths and practicalities of everyday commerce, so it must be with all forms of knowledge: to be valid it must conform with what is observed. This reluctance to use observation and measurement in a systematic way, may have been a reflection of social prejudice, which separated the *superior* activities of mind from the *inferior* practical work of the craftsman. In an Egyptian papyrus of about 1100 BC one finds this admonition of a father to his son:

> Put writing in your heart that you may protect yourself from hard labour of any kind . . . The scribe is released from all manual tasks; it is he who commands. I have seen the metal worker at his task at the mouth of his furnace, with fingers like a crocodile. He stank worse than fish-spawn. I have not seen a blacksmith on a commission, a founder who goes on an embassy.[3]

In societies like these, balanced perspectives on the importance of tools, craft and observational practice were perhaps unlikely to develop. Segregation of the intellectual from craft work would inevitably discourage the appearance of any sort of experimental approach. The concept of an experiment could hardly find expression against a backdrop of contempt for the practical — one reason, perhaps, why Egyptian and Babylonian science failed to advance much after the middle of the second millennium. Other factors enhanced this stagnation. Mesopotamia, for instance, succumbed to invasion by mounted hordes out of the north and east. In Egypt the growing power of a dogmatic priesthood led to a long period of intellectual stagnation.

Another high culture, that of the Minoans on the island of Crete also reached its zenith during the middle of the second millennium BC. But its records have only been partially deciphered, and we cannot say much about its scientific competence. We know only that the Minoans used arithmetic in a form borrowed, probably, from the Egyptians. After dominating the Aegean for many centuries they suffered the huge volcanic explosion of Thera (Santorini) — c. 1650 BC according to recent datings of volcanic dust layers in the Greenland ice-cap — and associated earthquakes, followed by invasion from the north. They never fully recovered from these catastrophes; after about 1200 BC — the beginning of the Homeric age — their history merges with that of Ionia.

In Greece, the Aegean and the Near East, the period between about 1200 and 700 BC marks the transition from bronze to iron. It was a period of invasions, migrations, chaos and obscurity; George Sarton refers to it as a Dark Age. Very little progress occurred in the sciences. The restless Phoenicians, who inherited the Cretan dominance of the Aegean and established outposts all over the Mediterranean (Carthage), bequeathed us an alphabet but no science to speak of. One must wait till the Greek Renaissance in the seventh century BC — the birth of *the Greek Miracle* — to see learning flourish again. This it did first with the Greek colonists of Ionia on the coast of Asia Minor and, after their culture shifted westward, with the city states on the Greek mainland.

Ionia, in what is now Western Anatolia, had been settled by emigrants from Crete and mainland Greece. It is a land of deep fertile valleys separated by great east-west mountain ribs, huge tiers of limestone plunging into the sparkling blue waters of the Aegean. In the winter the high mountain ridges turn white and the air is crystalline. 'The air and the climate', says Herodotus, 'are the most beautiful in the whole world.' Sometime in the ninth or eighth centuries, Ionia saw the birth of the Illiad and the Odyssey. Homer's vast masterpiece appears suddenly — its origins obscure, its author an uncertain and mysterious figure. It contains little of direct relevance to the history of science, but it was a forerunner — an indication of the intellectual ferment which was to change the face of the world. As the centuries went by, Homer's writings were to be read reverentially by all educated Greeks — acquiring a status comparable to that of the sacred Scriptures of our own culture. Their influence on Greek thought was profound, even if their connection to early science appears tenuous. And so George Sarton has remarked, in a characteristic passage, that, centuries later, the study of Homeric geography may well have stimulated Eratosthenes' great works.

The ancient city of Miletos was the pride of Ionia. Its four harbours were the focus of trade with Egypt, Phoenicia, Rhodos, the Cyclades and Sporades, Chios, Lesbos, the Hellespont and Black Sea ports. With its colonies extending from the Nile to the sea of Azov and the estuary of the Don, it was powerful and prosperous. Caravan routes from the East ran not far inland; some reached into Miletos. The city itself stood on a limestone promontory between two gulfs. Silt from the river Meander has long ago changed these into swamps; the glory that was Miletos is no more. But in the sixth century BC it was a rich prize, an irresistible lure for scheming Persian kings.

The Ionian and Greek miracle was to be the crowning of Eastern Mediterranean culture. Why did it begin in Ionia? One may conjecture that the early Ionian colonists were an enterprising and energetic group. Like all emigrants — like the Pilgrim Fathers of New England 2,500 years later — they had to be resourceful and independent-minded, ready to question old answers and seek new solutions. A great deal of mixing occurred in Ionian ports; the Phoenicians came with knowledge of far lands to the west; caravan routes brought news of the Orient; mathematical and astronomical competence arrived from Egypt and the East — from Babylon and elsewhere. It was a time not only of ferment, but of tension and anxiety too. Pressure from the Persians increased through the sixth century, and was eventually to push Greek culture westwards on to the mainland (500 BC). Whatever the influences at work, the accomplishments of the sixth century Ionian philosophers are impressive. Most of their activity was centred in Miletos.

Miletos' earliest and most celebrated philosopher and scientist was *Thales* (624-545 BC). Probably of Phoenician extraction, he must have witnessed the conquest of most of Ionia by Cyrus the Great — of which, it is said, he had warned his fellow countrymen. Little is known about him, beyond the fact that he travelled to Egypt, whence he brought back a knowledge of astronomy and geometry. Highly regarded by his contemporaries, he was, with Solon of Athens, one of Ionia's *Seven Wise Men*. Like many a philosopher since, he was absent-minded — he is said to have fallen into a ditch while looking at the stars. Nevertheless, like a good Ionian, he also had a fine nose for business, and got rich by speculating on olive oil. Aristotle reports that

> Thales knew by his skill in the stars while it was yet winter that there would be a great harvest of olives in the coming year; so, having a little money, he gave deposits for the use of all the olive-presses in Chios and Miletos, which he hired at a low price because no one bid against him. When the harvest time came, and many were wanted all at once and of a sudden, he let them out at any rate which he pleased, and made a quantity of money. Thus he showed the world that philosophers can easily be rich if they like, but that their ambition is of another sort.[2]

An early claim perhaps, for the power of scientific knowledge . . .

He is also alleged to have used his astronomical knowledge to predict the eclipse of 585, but the legend is suspect. Perhaps Thales' greatest accomplishment was to extend the geometry of the Egyptians and Babylonians and change it into a systematic, rigorous discipline. Whereas they had obtained their theorems by generalizing from measurements (induction), Thales was the first to prove such theorems by deduction from simpler cases — a process which was to be extended by his student Pythagoras. He may thus be seen as the founder of geometry as we know it — the axiomatic geometry which, centuries after his death, would attain such perfection in Euclid's *Elements*. This, said Kant, makes Thales the father of a genuine intellectual revolution. He was also a practical man and observed carefully the properties of the lodestone — thereby initiating the study of magnetism. Aristotle quotes him as saying

That the magnet has a soul in it because it moves the iron.[3]

Remarkable, too, was Thales' effort to create a unified theory of the world. He is the first on record to have attempted this by assuming a single fundamental constituent for all matter; in the vernacular of the philosophers, this makes him the first *monist*. As his basic constituent he chose water — which, for a man of his time, was not such a wild notion. Water, after all, seems to occur everywhere: as a solid in the winter snow and ice of the high mountains of Asia Minor, as dew, rain and seawater, and as steam in the boiling pot; it comes pouring out of the sky, it spurts mysteriously from cracks in the rock and it laps endlessly, in inexhaustible quantities, along the shores of the blue Aegean. So while he was wrong, his was an intellectually responsible idea — a genuine effort at a unified theory of the universe. In this sense Thales was the earliest theoretical physicist and perhaps the first pure scientist.

Another great Milesian was *Anaximander* (610-545). Thales' contemporary and his junior by fourteen years, he may have been his disciple. He wrote the first treatise on Natural Philosophy — of which, alas, only a few lines survive. He too was a monist; but he proposed an alternative to Thales' theory. Instead of accepting water as the basic constituent of all matter, he invented an abstract concept, an intangible substance called apeiron. This idea, precocious and unrefined, was also a step in the direction of increasing abstraction — a direction science has followed more recently: today's model of quarks and leptons is as intangible as Anaximander's. The main difference is that ours predicts measurable, quantitative phenomena: it gives us *power* over our world. Anaximander's or Thales' theories did little beyond offering a somewhat spurious *philosophical* unity. But we must not be harsh; these early efforts showed a truly modern imagination — they were almost prescient.

Anaximander's anticipation was also remarkable in other fields; he postulated a principle of biological adaptation and man's descent from the animals:

'Man was like another animal, namely a fish, in the beginning.'[3]

Anaximenes (died *c.* 525), the third major Milesian philosopher, found Anaximander's abstractions little to his taste and reintroduced something more tangible: he took air as the fundamental constituent of matter. Like Thales and Anaximander he conceived the earth as a freely suspended disc — a cosmological model almost certainly inherited from the Babylonians.

Fifty miles north of Miletos was the rich, and frequently sacked, market town of Collophon. *Xenophanes* (570-470?) was educated here. Said to have eventually settled in Elea (Castellamare di Veglia), he was, with Parmenides, a founder of the Eleatic school of philosophy. According to a later writer, Hippolytes, he must be seen as the first geologist and paleontologist:

> And Xenophanes is of the opinion that there had been a mixture of the earth with the sea, and that in the process of time it was disengaged from the moisture, alleging that he could produce such proofs as the following: that in the midst of earth and mountains shells are discovered; and also in Syracuse he affirms was found in the quarries the print of a fish and of seals, and in the Paros the print of an anchovy in the bottom of a stone, and in Malta parts of all sorts of marine animals. And he says that these were generated when all things were originally embedded in mud, and that an impression of them was dried in mud . . .[2]

Clearly a man of powerful intuition, he was also a free thinker and a sceptic: 'There is,' he said, 'nowhere anything but guessing.'[4]

When the Persians pushed Ionian culture westward, many of the new immigrants did not stop in Greece, but went further west, to what is now southern Italy and Sicily. The most famous was *Pythagoras*, the greatest of the Pre-Socratics, perhaps the most important mathematician of all time and, in his youth, a disciple of Thales. Once more, what we know of his life is a mixture of myth, apocrypha and hagiography. He was born around 580 BC in Samos — an island less than thirty miles west of Miletos. He grew and flourished there for a time, then left — either from fear of Polycrates, the local tyrant, or to escape the Persians. He then travelled widely, absorbing, among other things, the ancient wisdom of Babylon and Egypt. Late in life he reached and settled in Croton, in southern Italy, and established there his school which, at its height, numbered three to four hundred men and women. His love of mathematics and feeling for number bordered on the mystical. Disciples and well-wishers were to foist upon him the fatherhood of a new religion called, logically enough, Pythagoreanism — an embarrassing position, one might think, for any mathematician to be caught in; but history does not record how Pythagoras himself felt about it. Suffice it to say that the Pythagoreans acquired much influence and power in the affairs of Croton — too much, it seems, since the population rebelled and the brotherhood was massacred or exiled. According to Sarton the master himself was to die in exile in Metapontion, *c.* 497.

Pythagoras made important contributions to astronomy and to knowledge of the Earth; he is often credited with discovering its sphericity and speculating about its motion (but the first suggestion that Earth might be merely one of several planets orbiting a 'central fire' was due to *Philolaos*, a fifth century Pythagorean).

Pythagoras discovered, too, many important properties of numbers and geometrical theorems. Perhaps his most seminal contribution to science, his greatest stroke of genius was his perception of the central importance of numbers for understanding the world. This appears first in his analysis of the overtones of a stretched string. Strung between two points a string gives, when plucked, a pure tone: the fundamental or ground note. Divide it into integral

parts — two, three, four, and so on, — and the resulting tones harmonize with the fundamental; they give the
chords which sound pleasing to the Western ear. This was
Pythagoras' great discovery — the one which, for him, bore
witness to the importance of numbers in the universe; it
gave him a deep respect for them and, in particular, for
the sequence of natural numbers or integers 1,2,3,4 . . . It
even misled him into believing that the distances between
heavenly bodies had to be related to integers and musical
intervals: the music of the spheres . . . Indeed, he saw
numbers not, like we do today, as symbols but as the ultimate reality.

Pythagoras did not limit the role of number to what he could
hear; he applied it also to what he could *see*, using his insight
into number theory to prove geometrical theorems — such as
the celebrated one which bears his name and says that, in a
right angle triangle, the square of the hypothenuse equals the
sum of the squares of the other two sides. Arguably the most
important single theorem in mathematics, it expresses better
than any other our perception of space as we encounter it in
everyday life; it crops up again and again in modern mathematics, in theoretical physics and in our earliest wrestlings with
school geometry. It is reported that when Pythagoras proved
this theorem, he was so elated that he sacrificed an ox to the
gods.

As for Pythagoras' cosmology, it was ruled by a mixture
of myth and aesthetics. The sphere being the most *perfect* of
solids, the universe was divided into three spherical regions:
Uranos (the Earth or sublunary sphere), Cosmos (the move-
able heavens), Olympos (the abode of the gods). Likewise the
various astronomical bodies moved in uniform circular motion
because the circle was the perfect geometrical figure — an
assumption which was to plague astronomers for more than
two thousand years.

Pythagoras was not a practical man; he had little interest in using knowledge as a tool for power. In fact he is
on record as asserting the value of pure science, regardless
of possible applications. The pursuit of disinterested knowledge, said he, is the greatest purification. As Sarton has put
it:[2]

> He (Pythagoras) was the first to connect love of science with sanctity. He might well be feted as the patron saint of men of science of all ages, the pure theorists, the contemplators.'

In the fifth century, almost matching Pythagores' reputation, came *Empedocles of Agrigentium* (492-430). Nominally a Pre-Socratic philosopher, he was almost a contemporary of Socrates, being his senior by a scant twenty years. He marked a significant break with the Milesian philosophers in that he believed the world to consist of four basic substances — water, air, earth and fire — a view which was to dominate western thinking almost until the eighteenth century. In contradistinction to the Milesian philosophers, this makes him the first *pluralist*.

Empedocles is justly famed for having conducted the earliest recorded deliberate experiment in the history of physics, using a clepsydra — a vessel with a hole at each end to demonstrate the corporeality of air. Plunging it under water whilst keeping a finger on the upper hole he observed, upon releasing his finger, bubbles of air travelling to the surface of the water. Simple and childish as it may appear to us today, someone had to be the first to make this observation *and* draw the correct conclusion — such insights only look easy with the wisdom of hindsight.

According to Aristotle, Empedocles also worried about the propagation of light:

> Empedocles says that the light from the sun arrives first in the intervening space before it comes to the eye, or reaches the Earth. This might plausibly seem to be the case. For whatever is moved (in space) is moved from one place to another; hence, there must be a corresponding interval of time also in which it is moved from one place to the other. But any given time is divisible into parts; so that we should assume a time when the sun's ray is not yet seen, but was still travelling in the middle space.[2]

His physiological and medical observations were equally remarkable; he studied the inner ear and he postulated a degree of respiration through the skin. Alongside his many scientific activities he was a poet, a doctor and led an enterprising life as a social reformer — acquiring, like Pythagoras, an almost preternatural reputation for wisdom. Legends — complimentary or scurrilous — surround his name. According to one, he died by jumping into the crater of Etna, trying to show that he was a god. Bertrand Russell, in his History of Western Philosophy, could not refrain from quoting the ditty:[4]

> Great Empedocles, that ardent soul,
> Leapt into Etna, and was roasted whole.

But, according to Bernard Williams, the story is false.[5]

We possess a little more knowledge of these Pre-Socratic men of science than of their Babylonian and Egyptian predecessors, but our information is still woefully scant. We know hardly anything about their persona, appearance, emotions or family lives; snippets of biography, fragments of thought have filtered down through the ages — either directly, via their writings, or second-hand, as retold by pupils, friends, enemies or later writers. A few words reach out to us, spanning the millennia, words saying, in effect: we were here once, we too strove after the truth, we started you out on your present quest. Much of what they said was speculative and much of it was wrong. But some of it was true and their truths were both powerful and beautiful. Most had little, if any, overt interest in *applying* their science. Nevertheless, as any mathematical physicist will tell you, Pythagoras' theorem has helped shape our world in ways far more enduring than all the Trojan wars or Persian empire-building.

CHAPTER FIVE

Athens

By the close of the sixth century BC the Persians had subjugated
most of Ionia. Miletos, the jewel of the eastern Mediterranean,
its position insecure, had been pressured into collaborating. In
a desperate bid for independence, supported by Athens, but not
by Sparta, it led the Ionian rebellion — the beginning of which c.
499 coincided, to within a year or two, with Pythagoras' death.
Poorly led, betrayed by its allies, Miletos was sacked by Darius'
troops in 494. The Persians revenge was characteristically savage — they killed every male, took all women and children into
slavery and razed the city so completely it never recovered.
After this, pressure on the Greek mainland increased. In the war
that followed the Greeks showed both heroism and inspiration,
first defeating a much larger Persian army at Marathon (490).
Their decisive triumph was the naval victory of Salamis (480),
historically perhaps the most significant battle of all time; had
Xerxes' fleet been victorious, the course of Greek culture — and
our own — could have been entirely different. The encounter
at Salamis was followed by one last devastating victory over the
Persians near Plataea in the Boeotian plain in 479. This marked
the beginning of the Athenian period. For fifty years, mostly
under the stewardship of Pericles, Athens was supreme.

Pericles brought to Athens the philosopher *Anaxagoras* (488-
428), a pupil of Anaximenes. He is best remembered for his
suggestion that the sun was a molten rock — a piece of
inventiveness which earned him a charge of impiety and
exile. He also preached the infinite divisibility — the *continuity*
— of matter. Like his Milesian teacher he thought the Earth to
be a cylindrical disc. Motion he believed to be a manifestation
of mind or soul.

Whilst he is classed by philosophers as a Pre-Socratic, his life
overlapped the period of Socrates and of the great philosophi-

cal and literary explosion of fifth-century Athens.

This was the age of Socrates, Sophocles, Aeschylus, Euripides, Aristophanes, Hippocrates — a period of literary and philosophic achievement never equalled again anywhere, anytime. It was also the first attempt at democratic government in Western history (women and slaves, however, were excluded from the process). But the golden years of Athens proved all too few. In 431 Sparta — aristocratic, totalitarian, and war-like, prodded by economically hard-pressed allies, jealous of Athens' glory — embarked upon the Peloponnesian wars (431-421, 414-404), eventually crushing Athens. As if the horrors of war were not enough, Athens was ravaged by the plague (430-425). It was the end of an era; to the Athenians it must have looked like the end of the world. Yet their culture survived these disasters; Greek science and philosophy, in fact, continued to prosper — then and for a long time thereafter.

The great age of philosophy begins with Socrates (470-399) and continues unabated, through war and pestilence, until the death of Aristotle in 322. Many, and particularly philosophers, regard this as Greece's Golden Age. A historian of science, however, could argue that the previous hundred years had been both more seminal and more original; he/she might also claim, with some justification, that the effect of the greatest philosophers of this age — Socrates, Plato and Aristotle — had not always been good for science. But for philosophy this was an extraordinary time. Plato was a disciple of Socrates and Aristotle a disciple of Plato: a concatenation of genius unparalleled in history. This revered trinity of philosophers was to put its mark on the millenia to come.

Despite their close ties, they were remarkably different.

Son of a sculptor and midwife, *Socrates* was born in Athens. He developed an early interest in philosophy and politics — discussion and rhetoric were an integral part of the Athenian scene. Homely, robust and unpretentious, Socrates was a good soul. Argumentative, always on the verge of destitution, he asked little of the world — mainly, that it listen to him talk. His mature years coincided with the Peloponnesian wars and the collapse of Athenian democracy; hardly surprising, then, that his most significant thinking dealt with ethical and political issues. Like so many men of wisdom before and since, he became a thorn in the side of his government. Given the choice of escape or death, he chose the latter. A wise man, he said, respects the law and doesn't fear dying. And so he drank the hemlock with composure and good grace.

Yet, while Socrates was, in human affairs, a man of great wisdom, he contributed little to scientific thought. It is of course difficult to be quite sure of this, since he left no writings of his own. His ideas come to us by way of Plato's dialogues and Xenophon's writings. The former had his own ideas to grind and the latter was, according to Russell,[1] 'a military man not very liberally endowed with brains'; either way we are unlikely to have Socrates' thoughts handed down to us unaltered. When the two concur, however, we can be reasonably certain of our ground. They agree, for instance, that Socrates was rather contemptuous of science. To quote Xenophon:

> He did not even discuss that topic so favoured of other talkers, 'the Nature of the Universe', and avoided speculation on the so-called 'Cosmos' of the Professors, how it works, and on the laws that govern the phenomena of the heavens: indeed he would argue that to trouble one's mind with such problems is sheer folly. In the first place, he would inquire, did these thinkers suppose that their knowledge of human affairs was so complete that they must seek new fields for the exercise of their brains; or that it was their duty to neglect human affairs and consider only things divine?[2]

(critics of today's technocratic establishment likewise point to the vast sums and energies spent on space exploration or high energy physics whilst urgent problems of poverty, starvation, disease and social injustice remain unsolved — *plus ça change, plus c'est la même chose*) Not surprisingly, historians of science devote little space to Socrates. Nevertheless, in an age when the distinction between science and philosophy had yet to be made, he contributed at least indirectly to the advancement of science — if only by his insistence on the importance of defining one's terms, his clarity of thought and his unwillingness to speculate.

Plato (428-347), Socrates' aristocratic and handsome pupil, was descended on his mother's side from Solon and, according to legend, from the god Poseidon on his father's. He fought in the last years of the Peloponnesian wars, and reached maturity in Athens during the period of chaos and dissolution which followed defeat. Opportunities for disinterested public service offered by this state of affairs being limited, he forsook involvement in politics. Socrates' death fuelled his contempt for demagogues and politicians, convincing him that no real improvement of society could take place until philosophers were kings or kings became philosophers. In 387 he founded the *Academy*, the purpose of which — described in *The Republic* — was to form philosophers fit to rule. The earliest Western institution of higher learning, it nurtured a number of great philosophers and 'scientists'.

Plato asked many of the questions that have, ever since, concerned philosophy. This makes him, arguably, the greatest Western philosopher of all time: Western philosophy, said Whitehead, is but footnotes to Plato.

The world's greatest philosopher was, among other things, its first epistemologist. It is to him that we owe the original distinction between concepts (forms) and perceptual data, a distinction he illustrated with the famous parable of the cave — in which prisoners, chained and unable to turn, see the world as moving shadows projected on the wall before them. Unless the prisoners are released from their bonds, they cannot grasp the existence of the real objects behind them — the source of the shadows, the *forms* accessible only to those who, liberated by a knowledge of philosophy, have cast off their chains. For the others, shadows — the everyday sensory world — are the sole reality. This is an essential and beautiful insight; it illuminates the whole problem of the relationship of knowledge to object. The mathematician's concept of a line is the idea or *form* of a line. The draughtsman's curve — or the particle's trajectory in a bubble chamber — are its sensory expressions — Plato's shadows. Plato's parable brings to mind also E.M. Forster's novelist, the myopic earthbound observer, with only a flickering shadow from which to reconstruct the form — the idea of a bird.[3]

Plato carried this insight rather further than one cares to follow him today. He believed literally in the reality and separateness of his forms — a concept which, he said, could only be fully understood by one trained in philosophy. He made it central to all his thinking. Modern philosophers tell us that Plato's theory of *universals* (as his forms are now called) does not stand up to detailed scrutiny — it raises too many logical difficulties. But the analogies it conjures up — be it Plato's cave or the shadow of Forster's bird — are as suggestive as ever of the relationship between concepts and observation.

Science, or at least post-Renaissance science, operates systematically with both shadow and form. Form is the theory or mathematical model — the framework of any true science; it is born of shadow — the experimental 'realities' of our laboratories. In science these two categories — theory and experiment — must interact in essential ways; they feed upon each other. No Greek was to articulate this *obligatory* interaction. In his biological work, Aristotle came close; but, as a general *modus operandi* in the quest of knowledge it was not to be achieved for two thousand years. The causes for this must be complex. But a contributory factor, surely, was cultural bias. The Greeks despised manual work — like the Egyptians before them, theirs was a slave economy. Thus Xenophon:

> What are called the mechanical arts carry a social stigma, and are rightly dishonoured in our cities.

Plato, the aristocrat, reflected this attitude in his social theories as well as in his epistemology. He saw the role of forms as intrinsically superior to that of sensory reality, just as he saw craftsmen as inferior to philosophers. This led him to conclusions which were actually inimical to the development of science. Thus in *Phaedo* he says that philosopy

> bids the soul trust in itself and its own sure appreciation of pure existence, and distrust whatever comes to it through other channels subject to variation . . .[4]

Today's scientist — the modern natural philosopher — will agree on the importance of form if this is equated with theory, but not at the expense of shadow (i.e., the sensory, experimental input). The history of science strongly suggests that these are complementary and must interact, if science is to be a healthy, growing process.

Plato raised a host of questions that had never been asked

before: he *is* the king of philosophers. Yet historians of science have sometimes condemned his influence because his natural philosophy remained at all times subordinate to his theory of forms (and to his social and theological views). This led him to *a priori* edicts on the nature of matter, the stars and the universe which, according to some were, scientifically speaking, reckless.[5] He constructed a universe from simple geometrical elements — right-angle triangles.

Espousing Empedocles' theory of four elements, he ruled that their forms were those of the regular polyhedra. He embellished Pythagoras' theories of the heavens, stating that the stars and the planets were divine and supernatural beings moving uniformly in perfect circles. As Sarton has observed *Timaios*, Plato's main scientific work, is full of unwarranted analogies between the human soul and the soul of the universe, replete with astrological and numerological nonsense. He believed in reincarnation, stating that men who led bad lives 'were suitably reborn as women in the second generation' and 'beasts who go on all fours came from men who were wholly unconversant with philosophy'. In a lesser man, these would have been harmless conceits; but his reputation as a philosopher was so formidable that much of what he said influenced people for centuries. 'One thing I know, and that is that I know nothing' said Socrates; had his star pupil been as modest, the science of succeeding ages, says Sarton, might have moved faster. Yet such judgments are suspect. It is entirely possible to defend, as Feyerabend does,[6] the opposite view and claim that astronomy may have actually profited from Pythagoreanism and from Plato's circles. However that may be, there shines in all of Plato's writings a light of pure, unsullied love of knowledge. No one may question Plato's intentions — not even when, as in *The Republic*, he is at his most reactionary. He died honoured and loved by many.

In Plato's lifetime, already, the Balkan strand in Greek history had begun to stir. Philip II of Macedonia, himself part Greek, became king in 360 BC and took it upon himself to unify the political chaos that was Greece. By 338 he had impressed his will and established the Hellenic League, which included all the Greek states except Sparta. Ruthless and dissolute, he was murdered in 336. The life of his son *Alexander the Great* was short

(356-323), but his effect on the history of the Mediterranean and the Near East was telling. He crushed the Persians; he extended Greek influence as far as India; he brought East and West together and thereby permanently affected the course of history. Today, rather naturally, we view military rulers — especially conquerors — with suspicion. Alexander, however, must be judged in the context of his time — an age in which Hellenistic culture, its humanistic aspirations, its philosophy and science were threatened by Persia, Carthage and northern barbarian tribes; an age when murder, war and pillage were, all too often, the proper and accepted coinage of power. Seen in this light Alexander cuts an altogether more favourable figure than, let us say, Genghis Khan or Napoleon. In many ways he was an interesting and surprisingly generous man.[7] The Greeks had always regarded foreigners either as enemies or as inferiors — as serfs or slaves. Alexander rejected these views. He married a Bactrian princess; he encouraged the mixing of races and intermarriage between his men and natives of his empire; he perceived humanity's essential unity. His phenomenal conquests did, eventually, go to his head and he could behave as cruelly and arbitrarily as any potentate; yet, according to some historians, he did not so much dream of world empire as of a world brotherhood of men.

Like Alexander, *Aristotle* (384-322) was a Macedonian. He came from Stageira, where his father had been physician to Amyntas II, Alexander's grandfather. At the age of seventeen he was sent to Athens, to study at the Academy. He remained there, on and off, for close to twenty years. Plato quickly recognized his gifts and described him as 'intelligence personified'. After Plato's death he travelled for some time, then, for two years (342-340), became Alexander's tutor. Upon his return to Athens in 335 he may have found that his Macedonian connection made him unwelcome with former colleagues. He started his own institution of higher learning, which he called the *Lyceum* — a sort of early model Academy of Sciences with educational functions. In this he received material assistance from his famous pupil. It is said that Alexander, on his great expeditions, sent rocks, minerals and plants to Aristotle for study. After Alexander's death in 323, the reaction against the Macedonians became very strong. Saying that he did not wish the Athenians to sin twice against philosophy, Aristotle fled to Chalcis, where he died within a few months.

Temperamentally, Aristotle was very different from Plato; yet in important respects they were complementary. In contrast to Plato's idealistic and theoretical proclivities, Aristotle was an empiricist. For Plato mathematics was the queen of the sciences; Aristotle's intellectual commitment was in large measure to observation and biology. He modified Plato's views on forms accordingly. For Aristotle *form* was simply one aspect of *this* world — not separate from the object of our senses, even if distinguishable in thought. Either form or matter without the other is unreal. But, as any biologist is well aware, matter changes — the child turns into an adult, the acorn into an oak. Aristotle therefore introduced notions of the ideal and the possible — i.e., actuality and *potentiality*. For him potentiality is the end purpose of a thing, essential to its understanding. This is the concept of *teleology* — a point of view which appears to arise naturally in the study of a myriad life forms so obviously adapted to their environments. Most likely, it retarded the development of science: for centuries it encouraged sloppy thinking, leading people to explain away phenomena by appealing to some purpose. In defense of Aristotle one has to say that, at first glance, teleology often *seems* plausible in biological contexts: 'Oh, grandmother, what big teeth you have!' 'The better to eat you with, my dear!' As Bernal puts it: the big bad wolf was 'a perfect Aristotelian and not too bad an ecologist.'[8]

Aristotle saw *purpose* as the most important type of *cause* operating in Nature: he called this the *final* cause. He classified all causes into four kinds, the other three being: *efficient* causes (mechanism: the *how* of things), *formal* causes (relating to shape or design), *material* causes (constitutive material). Consider a house: stone or wood is the material cause, the architect's design supplies the formal cause; the stonemason's and carpenter's crafts are the efficient causes and the house's purpose is the final cause. For Aristotle this last was critical: understanding purpose alone threw light on the true nature of things. As Plato had believed that the transcendent form explains particular sensory experiences, so Aristotle felt that knowing the purpose of a thing (his definition of form) was necessary for proper understanding. This applies well enough to man-made objects like houses, but, in all likelihood, not at all to nature.

Aristotle created logic as a discipline and wrote the first treatises on the subject: their ensemble is the *Organon* — a work venerated and enthusiastically exploited by medieval philosophers. While recognizing its greatness as a pioneering work, modern logicians are less keen about it. According to Bertrand Russell, even today its influence 'is so inimical to clear thinking that it is hard to remember how great an advance he made upon all his predecessors (including Plato), or how admirable his logical work would seem if it had been a stage in a continual progress, instead of being (as in fact it was) a dead end, followed by over two thousand years of stagnation.'[1] Aristotle invented the syllogism, a classic example of which is: *Socrates is a man. All men are mortal. Therefore Socrates is mortal*. Like many a lesser mortal he misapplied the procedure at times — if only because his premises were occasionally wrong. Air, said he, is necessary for violent motion (wrong). Violent motion exists in the sublunary world (right). Therefore the sublunary world is full of air, i.e., a vacuum is impossible.

Aristotle's other classic syllogistic *faux-pas* was a rejection of what would someday be known as Newton's first law of motion. He held that a body could maintain its motion only so long as it was in contact with a mover — a view which appeared to resolve Zeno's famous paradox. Zeno of Elea (b.488) had pointed to a logical difficulty involved in motion along a line. A line is an infinite collection of points; but, he reasoned, an arrow shot along a line had to be, at a given instant, at rest with respect to some given point on this line; it would, he suggested, never reach its destination. This is the arrow paradox: as one wit has put it, if Zeno was right, Saint Sebastian died of fright. The problem was in fact difficult and would only be resolved, a couple of millenia later, with modern continuity concepts. Aristotle attempted to remove the fallacy, as he called it, by ruling that air rushes in to fill the space left behind and acts as a mover. This became a central tenet of mechanics — and remained so for seventeen hundred years. Another equally erroneous cornerstone of Aristotelian (and medieval) physics was the teleological explanation of gravity:

bodies fell because everything seeks its natural place at the centre of the universe (i.e., of the Earth).

Aristotelian cosmology, partly inherited from Pythagoras, partly developed by contemporaries like Eudoxos, assumed the existence of concentric rotating spheres carrying planets and stars. The Earth was part of the sublunary sphere — for which Aristotle accepted Empedocles' four elements as material causes (earth, water, air and fire). The heavenly sphere was composed of a superior element — *the quintessence*. The outermost (also material) sphere of the fixed stars was moved by the *Unmoved Mover* (*Primum Mobile*). Like Pythagoras, Aristotle believed that the perfection of heavenly bodies required that their motions be circular and uniform.

What we now call the 'natural sciences' were Aristotle's strongest field — one in which he did much first-hand observing, thereby all but establishing an 'experimental method'. His chicken embryo study, given in the *History of Animals*, is a classic of systematic observation. In a search for formal causes he dissected a great many animals and classified over five hundred species. He foresaw the anatomical connection between birds and reptiles, and understood the close ties between humans and apes — and between humanity and the rest of the animal kingdom. Yet, like most of his contemporaries, he applied his observing skills erratically. His theory of mechanics implied that an arrow would follow an upward path and then, suddenly, drop like a stone; casual observation would have shown him that this could not be true. Even in biological matters he could be sloppy, as in his assertion that women had fewer teeth than men — an error he could have avoided, says Bertrand Russell, by asking Mrs Aristotle to keep her mouth open while he counted.[9] Nevertheless, apart from these lapses, Aristotle was the first Greek philosopher-scientist to make systematic, conscious efforts to ascertain the empirical facts — in the natural sciences. One may say that his philosophy of science, a combination of induction and deduction, would not be bettered for almost two thousand years.

Aristotle's biological work — much of it valid — remained insufficiently appreciated until after it had been superseded. It is ironic that, at the same time, his wrong-headed speculations on motion *were* accepted, and may have done much to retard the progress of physics.

Aristotle was succeeded at the Lyceum by a student of his, *Theophrastos of Eresos* (372-287). Faithful to his teacher's insistence on the need to observe, he was primarily a natural scientist and a botanist; many of the names he gave to plants survive until this day. His views on cause were more modern than Aristotle's: he maintained that efficient causes (mechanism) rather than final causes (purpose) are the proper concern of science. He wrote the first treatise on minerals and gems, recognizing and listing many minerals familiar to the modern mineralogist. He was the last major scientist of the Aristotelian age.

A distinguished contemporary of Socrates and Plato was *Hippocrates* — to this day a physician's paragon. Born c. 460, he came from a medical (Asclepiad) family of renown. Plato and Aristotle are known to have thought highly of him. He lived to a ripe old age (eighty-five or so), a fact which is unlikely to have had much to do with his knowledge of medicine; Hippocratic practice was far more adept at diagnosis and prognosis than at curing the patient. The writings of his school, which go under the rather ponderous name of the *Hippocratic Corpus*, are a detailed account of the medical arts of early Greece; this is mostly a lengthy description of symptoms and precepts for doctors. No one knows which parts of the *Corpus*, if any, were actually written by Hippocrates; scholars of all ages have tended to ascribe to Hippocrates the works that they themselves happened to value most highly.[10]

The age of Socrates, Plato, Aristotle and Hippocrates — a period spanning a century and a half — saw much progress in science. Many philosopher-scientists left remarkable and indelible marks on the history of thought. Less may be known about them than of Socrates or Plato but, for the historian of science, some were more important. There was, for example, *Democritos of Abdera* (460-370?). A contemporary of Socrates (whom he saw, but was too shy to introduce himself) he is most famous as the probable inventor of atomism. While he was certainly beholden to his teacher Leucippos — and to Oriental sources — for some of his ideas, he is thought to have been the first to formulate a comprehensive atomistic view of the universe. He did this not on experimental grounds, but on philosophical and logical ones — often using arguments that sound quite modern. Aristotle would, of course, find himself in disagreement with Democritos for, if atoms existed, they had to move in a vacuum — the existence of which the great master of the syllogism had disproved! Aristotle's authority did much to retard the acceptance of atomism; nevertheless, Democritos' dream survived. But it would take more than twenty-three centuries for Western science to 'prove' the existence of atoms and molecules from chemical and physical data. Democritos' percipience was unusual in other spheres, too: he was the first to suggest that the Milky Way consisted of huge numbers of unresolved stars. He also propounded the first interjectional theory of the origins of speech — according to which language originated from animal-like emotional noises or interjections.

Perhaps the greatest scientific figure of the period was *Eudoxos of Cnidos* (408-355?). For the scientist, indeed, the Golden Age of philosophy may well be called the Age of Eudoxos.[5] He went to Athens at the age of twenty-three and became a pupil of Plato. He travelled to Egypt where it is reported that the sacred bull Apis licked his cloak, and the priests augured he would be famous but would not live long. In fact he died at the age of fifty-three — a fairly tender age, for a Greek philosopher. He certainly became the greatest mathematician and astronomer of his day. It may even be that he was the greatest mathematician of all time. Two thousand years before Newton and Leibniz, he all but invented the integral calculus — showing rigorously, for a polygon inscribed in a circle, how to increase indefinitely the number of sides whilst decreasing their length, thus passing to the limit and defining a circle (the method of *exhaustions*). And he introduced irrationals into number theory.

Eudoxos was also the first *scientific* astronomer, in that he understood the value of empirical information, carried out numerous observations himself and erected an observatory in Cnidos. And he combined astronomical measurements with mathematics to produce the earliest *model* (theory), in the modern sense, of the motions of the heavenly bodies. The problem in his day, and for almost two thousand years to come, was to explain the wanderings of the planets — which seem, at times, to retrace their steps, describing strange loops against the background of fixed stars. As his contemporaries put it: how to *save the phenomena*? Eudoxos, influenced by Pythagorean and Platonic conceptions, suggested that the planets moved uniformly in circles on twenty-seven concentric spheres. The spheres themselves moved around different axes at various speeds; the model was geocentric — i.e., the Earth was at its centre. The Eudoxian model was wrong; but this is of no importance, for this, it seems, is how science progresses: from one incorrect model to the next, more adequate, yet still to be discarded someday. What is important about Eudoxos' achievement is that *it was a true mathematical-physical model, allowing a fair measure of prediction*. Furthermore, in contrast to Aristotle, Eudoxos never assumed his spheres to be real. His was the first step on a long and often crooked road — the first of a sequence of cosmological models of varying complexity and sophistication which was to end, someday, with Newton and modern physics. This was genius, Greek rationalism at its best — tempered by a measure of empiricism.

Eudoxos' picture of the solar system was soon challenged: *Heracleides of Pontos* (388-310?) proposed a partially sun-centred (heliocentric) model, suggesting that Venus and Mercury orbited the sun. But the sun, moon and other planets, he said, revolved about the Earth.

Epicuros of Samos (341-270) was another great philosopher whose intuition on matters scientific was remarkable. A gentle figure, who preached moderation in all things, he was most deeply concerned with ethics and the quest for happiness. His scientific interests appear to have been incidental to these pursuits — undertaken, largely, to secure peace of mind.[10] He espoused Democritos' atomism and introduced the quality of randomness into the motion of atoms, as a kind of capriciousness or swerve (*clinamen*). This he may have done deliberately to avoid the pitfalls of a fully deterministic universe and its threat to the freedom of will. Whereas the problem of free will still vexes philosophers, the introduction of indeterminism was finally — and fully — vindicated by quantum mechanics early in our century — another example, perhaps, of an ancient Greek's uncanny prescience.

The anticipations of Anaximander, Pythagoras, Democritos,

Epicuros and other early Greeks were dramatic, and their dedication to the pursuits of knowledge was wholly admirable. Yet an important ingredient was missing: they never applied themselves to practical questions. For while the Greeks were good enough at observing, they remained philosophers — idealists who, with few exceptions, were far more interested in the theory than in the mechanical arts or in the power these could confer. As a result, the essential role of experiment — and its interaction with theory — would not be clearly conceived for almost two thousand years. Apart from their mathematical discoveries, and a few remarkable observations (Pythagoras' harmonics, Aristotle's biology) their knowledge of the universe was largely speculative. In the absence of hard evidence it could not be other. Yet it behooves us today to reflect on how many of these speculations have returned to haunt us, more or less, as facts: atomism, randomness, evolution. We would do well, also, to analyze the roots of our own belief in science — to see how much of it is founded on evidence, and how much on faith.

CHAPTER SIX

Alexandria

On the western edge of the Nile delta, flanked by desert, Alexandria has had a long and turbulent history. Founded by Greeks, alternately savaged or occupied by Romans, Muslims, French and British, the size of its population fluctuating wildly through the centuries, it is today a sprawling city of more than two million people. It is a seaport, a centre of commerce, a city of white minarets in which many languages are spoken and many races meet. Filth and fastiduousness, holiness and sin, poverty and wealth live here in egregious proximity. It is a place where, in the words of Lawrence Durrell, 'a thousand dust-tormented streets are ruled by beggars and by flies'. It was, once, the scientific capital of the world.

Alexander's death in 323 BC, a year after the founding of Alexandria, was the beginning of a new era. His vast empire disintegrated. From Egypt to India, from the Persian Gulf to the Caspian, wars erupted between Alexander's generals — the *Wars of the Diadochoi* or wars of the successors, which were to continue, on and off, for fifty years. The Western sector of the empire divided itself into three parts — Macedonia and Greece (the Antigonids), Western Asia (the Seleucids) and Egypt (the Ptolemies). Hellenistic culture and science, however, endured in centres in Asia Minor, Southern Italy (Magna Graecia), Sicily. On the latter island Syracuse was, for a time, a centre of scientific activity; its fortunes, though, were uneasy and a long, drawn out conflict with Carthage was settled by Roman occupation in 212. The most important focus of scientific achievement was to be in Alexandria. Here, for several centuries, through the rise of Roman power, and later, of Christianity, knowledge flourished — so much so that historians of science refer to this as the Alexandrian period.

In 323 *Ptolemaios* I (*Soter, the Saviour*), a Macedonian general and close friend of Alexander — perhaps his half-brother — took over the satrapy of Egypt. He finished erecting the city Alexander had begun and, with his son *Ptolemaios II* — *Philadelphos* — (285-247) he founded and built in Alexandria the world's first, and probably finest ever, institute for advanced studies. Dedicated to the Muses, it was named the *Museum;* for centuries it would offer a haven — lodgings, salaries and a place to work — for scholars from everywhere. In designing the Museum the Ptolemies were guided by *Straton the Physicist* (*Physikos*) and by Athenian political exile, *Demetrios of Phaleron*.

Demetrios was not a man of science but a Greek politician and, very likely, an able administrator. His chief contribution was to the *Library*, one of the glories of ancient Alexandria, to which he donated his own extensive collection of books. The great Library which for seven centuries acted as a magnet for scholars from all over the world, was totally destroyed in the fourth century AD. It seems to have been housed in a structure of considerable magnificence — a fit place for the half a million volumes it contained at its zenith, volumes which, at the time, represented the sum total of western knowledge.

Born in the last quarter of the fourth century in Lampsachos, on the Asiatic side of the Hellespont, *Straton* had first been a student of Theophrastos at the Lyceum, then a tutor to the future Ptolemaios II. Like his teacher, he was aware of the importance of empirical data and, like him, he was unsympathetic to the Aristotelian idea of final causes. It is thanks to Straton that the Museum became a *scientific* research institute. He was in Alexandria from about 300 to 288 when, following Theophrastos' death, he returned to Athens to direct the Lyceum. He died *c.* 270.

The first three Ptolemies were the most enterprising; they were also the most supportive in their relationships with the Museum. The great period of Alexandrian science coincides, roughly, with their reigns. Scholars and researchers were invited from abroad; many found the atmosphere stimulating and stayed. It is impossible to list them all, for there were hundreds. Three men, above all, attract our interest: Euclid, Aristarchos and Eratosthenes.

Euclid is an obscure figure. But his work endures — it has proved far less perishable than the Greek, Ptolemaic or Roman empires. We know neither when he was born nor when he died. Educated, probably, in Athens, it is thought that he learnt mathematics at the Academy towards the start of the third century. We know he lived in Alexandria at some stage of his career. Euclid's *Elements* is the only scientific treatise of any sort which, twenty-two centuries after its writing, can still be used profitably as a text. Starting from a few simple axioms, Euclid systematically deduced all the geometry known in his day — a paradigm of the deductive method, an example for all ages to come. Remarkable, uncanny almost, was Euclid's insight in selecting a complete set of axioms — five in all — in their simplest and most elegant form. In contrast to many other mathematicians — some well into the nineteenth century — he understood that the fifth, so-called parallel line, postulate, was a necessary adjunct to his geometry yet could not be proved.

Given a straight line, Euclid's fifth axiom says that, through a point, one can draw only one parallel to this line. This defines the kind of space Euclid thought we lived in — the so-called flat, or Euclidean, space. It took about twenty-two hundred years for this axiom to be re-examined. Three nineteenth century mathematicians — Lobachevski, Bolyai and Riemann — eventually showed that alternative geometries can be constructed using a different fifth axiom. This led, among other things, to the theory of new kinds of *curved* spaces. Imagine a small, flat two-dimensional being existing on a sphere, without any conception of height; the space he lives in is not Euclidean, but curved — the angles of his triangle do not add up to 180 degrees. Modern cosmologists believe our space is analogously curved in four dimensions. Euclid probably never conceived the possibility of such strange worlds; he went as far as genius could take him in the third century BC. For 2,200 years his fifth axiom stood unchallenged — an unused crossroads in our understanding of space and time. Only in our own century has Euclid's geometry yielded to Einstein's its place of privilege in describing the universe.

The figure of *Aristarchos of Samos* (310-230?) is equally vague. We know that he was a pupil of Straton — either in Alexandria or in Athens. We do not know where he composed his only surviving major work — a treatise entitled *On the Sizes and Distances of the Sun and Moon*. It is therefore on rather insufficient grounds that he is often classed as an Alexandrian astronomer. But wherever he worked, whatever his dates, his name looms large in the history of science.

The treatise, which has been preserved in full, is remarkable on two counts. In it, first of all, Aristarchos describes a correct method for measuring the sizes and distances of the moon and sun — providing one knows the size of the Earth and some basic astronomical data, such as the angle between moon and sun at half-moon (as seen from Earth). Second, all the derivations are carried out with Euclidean rigour. Unfortunately, Aristarchos used inaccurate data and his conclusions were seriously in error. However, an important series of new insights had been established and, with them, techniques for use by other astronomers. This alone would have assured Aristarchos' fame.

But he accomplised something even more interesting — in a work that has been lost. In his *Sand Reckoner*, Archimedes — a contemporary of Aristarchos — tells us about it:

> . . . cosmos is the name given by most astronomers to the sphere whose centre is the centre of the Earth, and whose radius is equal to the distance between the centre of the sun and the centre of the Earth. This is the common account as you have heard from astronomers. But Aristarchos of Samos brought out a book consisting of some hypotheses, wherein it appears, as a consequence of assumptions made, that the (real) universe is many times greater than the one just mentioned. His hypotheses are that the fixed stars and the sun remain unmoved, that the Earth revolves about the sun in the circumference of a circle, the sun lying in the middle of the orbit, and that the sphere of fixed stars, situated about the same centre as the sun, is so great that the circle in which he supposes the Earth to revolve bears such a proportion to the distance of the fixed stars as the centre of the sphere bears to its surface.

In other words, eighteen centuries before Copernicus, Aristarchos had conceived a fully heliocentric model of the solar system. He clearly saw the immense increase in the size of the universe that this entailed; the Earth's orbit had to be very small in comparison with the distances to the fixed stars (or their relative positions in the sky would change with the seasons!). This was an idea of exceptional intellectual boldness.

Cleanthes of Assos, a stoic philosopher, promptly suggested that Aristarchos be indicted for impiety:

> for moving the hearth of the universe and trying to save the phenomena by the assumption that the heavens is at rest, but that the Earth revolves on an oblique orbit, while revolving around its own axis.[1]

Humanity, it seems, was not ready for the view that it was not at the hub of the universe. Eighteen hundred years later, the idea would still prove unpalatable to many contemporaries of Copernicus and Galileo.

Eratosthenes of Cyrene (284-192) belonged to the generation following Aristarchos; more is known about him. He was one of history's most distinguished polymaths: mathematician, geodesist, geographer, astronomer, philologist, historian of science, man of letters. Educated in Athens at the Academy and the Lyceum, he spent the last fifty years of his life in Alexandria. Here, under three successive Ptolemies, he prospered at the Museum as an alpha (senior) fellow and chief librarian, while keeping up his connections with the Lyceum and with Cyrene — the place of his birth and a major cultural centre.

A fine mathematician, his cleverness is enshrined in the *sieve of Eratosthenes* — a wonderfully simple algorithm for finding prime numbers. The work for which he is most famous is his measurement of the size of the Earth: he was the first geodesist. His instrumentation was simple: a device for measuring the angle of the sun, the *gnomon*, gave him the difference in the latitudes of Alexandria and Syene. Near Syene he is said to have observed how, at noon on solstice day, the sun shone straight down a well (the well of Eratosthenes still exists, on an island in the Nile). Knowing then the angle of the sun in Alexandria and the distance between the cities, simple geometry gave him the circumference of the Earth. Considering the simplicity of the method and the errors of measurement incurred, his result was amazingly accurate — 39,690 km as compared with the modern value of 40,120 km, good to almost one per cent.

Eratosthenes published a treatise on geography, of which only fragments survive. He studied winds and introduced an eight-pointed wind rose. He invented a method for doubling a cube, published a study of old Greek comedy, wrote a history of philosophy and science. Knowledge and science were by then fairly specialized; as a polymath he was suspect to his colleagues — and subject to back-biting. They nicknamed him *beta* — to imply that he was second-rate and described him as a jack of all trades. Scientists were as jealous of their territories (and of each other) then as they are today.

During the height of the Alexandrian period another fragment of Hellenistic culture was prospering in Sicily. Here, in Syracuse, *Archimedes* (287-212) spent much of his life; he also visited Alexandria.

Archimedes was primarily a mathematician and physicist — amongst the greatest the world has seen. Using Eudoxos' method of exhaustions, he derived basic formulae for the volumes and areas of spheres, cones, cylinders and other surfaces. He obtained a four figure approximation for *pi*. He wrote a profound treatise on spheroids and another on spirals — all without the advantage of modern mathematical tools. He also created two branches of theoretical mechanics: statics and hydrostatics; his famous buoyancy principle, and his probably apocryphal method of discovery while sitting in a bath, are known to all. His abstractions from observation, as in the theory of the lever — which could be deduced rigorously only by assuming ideal, massless, perfectly rigid levers — were absolutely modern in spirit.

At the same time, Archimedes was a surprisingly practical man. He came as near as any Greek to initiating an experimental approach to physics — closer, even, than Aristotle whose empiricism had been limited to biological observations and perhaps as close as Eratosthenes with his geodetic measurements. His reputation for inventiveness was legendary already during his life. He understood the power of knowledge: give me a lever and a fulcrum, he said, and I shall move the world. He perfected the Archimedean screw for raising water, invented compound pulleys as well as a device for setting ships on fire by focussing the sun's rays upon them, and designed all sorts of military machinery. He became a kind of mechanical engineer and consultant to his kinsman Hieron II of Syracuse — rather as Leonardo da Vinci would be to Lodovico il Moro (Leonardo's motives were probably financial; Archimedes was Hieron's relative and friend). One can, with some justice, regard Archimedes as the first scientist of stature to have been involved in what we call today, euphemistically, defense work. In fairness, he was rather contemptuous of these achievements. According to Plutarch, he regarded

> . . . as ignoble and sordid the business of mechanics and every sort of art which is directed to use and profit, placing his whole ambition in those speculations the beauty and subtlety of which are untainted by any admixture of the common needs of life.[2]

Archimedes requested that his friends engrave on his tombstone a mathematical diagram: a cylinder circumscribing a sphere. In the year 212, at the age of seventy-five, he was murdered during the sack of Syracuse by a Roman soldier who neither knew nor cared who he was. His tomb, with the diagram on it, was last seen by Cicero in 75 BC.

The works of Euclid, Aristarchos, Eratosthenes and Archimedes were the crown of Greek science. They introduced essentially modern attitudes in mathematics and in the scientist's relationship to the world, which was now seen as a place to be measured and rigorously analyzed. The key to physics — the discipline of dynamics — was still a long way off; its development had to await a proper experimental approach. But Archimedes had created statics and the theory of simple mechanical, labour-saving devices. Third century science had come a long way from the speculations of the Milesian philosophers.

In the second century BC, further developments took place. Of special importance for future progress in physics, mathematics and astronomy was the theory of conics due to *Apollonius of Perge*, a mathematician from Pergamum on the south coast of Asia Minor, and Archimedes' junior by twenty-five years. In his *Conica* he dealt, with Euclidean style and rigour, with the properties of ellipses, hyperbolas and parabolas — names he coined for the curves one gets by cutting a cone, at various angles, by means of a plane. This established the essential mathematics Kepler would need, seventeen hundred years later, to describe the solar system. Apollonius, however, was committed to the geocentric view. He spent a great deal of time altering Eudoxos' already highly complex system of circular orbits with epicylces, introducing eccentrics (circular orbits not centred on the Earth) and, generally speaking, doing his bit to 'save the phenomena'.

Apollonius spent most of his life in Alexandria, but the various books of the *Conica* were dedicated to Pergamenians. Some are dedicated off-handedly to Attalos I, king of Pergamum with 'Apollonius to Attalos, greeting' — Greek philosophers and mathematicians had no tradition of obsequiousness. We know neither the place nor time of Apollonius' death.

Apollonius' improved version of the Eudoxian solar system was further perfected by *Hipparchos of Nicea* (190-120?). This final, highly complex geocentric model was to be known eventually as the Ptolemaic system, and would dominate the thinking of astronomers until the Renaissance. Hipparchos explicitly rejected Aristarchos' heliocentric model — though it was being defended at the time by an outstanding Babylonian astronomer, Seleucos of Seleuceia. In this we cannot really blame Hipparchos — he was only being a good scientist: within the constraint of circular orbits, his model actually saved the phenomena rather better than Aristarchos'. His greatest and most permanent contribution to astronomy was the discovery of the precession of the equinoxes — due, we now know, to the top-like behaviour of the Earth spinning on its axis as it orbits the sun. This was made possible by his own very accurate observations and the use of older Greek and Babylonian star tables. Hipparchos was also a great mathematician — he invented trigonometry.

Three hundred years after Hipparchos, *Claudius Ptolemy* of Alexandria (85-165 AD) completed the model of the solar system that bears his name — including, along with all the refinements of his predecessors, several centuries worth of planetary observations. The result, published in his *Syntaxis*, — to be translated later as the *Almagest* — is a fantastically complicated system of circular motions, involving some eighty circles. Ptolemy, to his credit, pointed out that this was unlikely to be more than a mathematical convenience. The Ptolemaic system, in other words, was not so much a physical model as a method of keeping track of planetary motions — a kind of predictive algorithm which did not claim to represent reality. On the debit side, modern statistical analysis suggests that Ptolemy fudged observations to fit his model — behaviour of which modern scientists take a dim view. Yet we must, I think, forgive the great man: the importance, indeed the *sanctity*, of the experimental input was simply not understood in his time.

As a geographer, Ptolemy provided a long, systematic list of longitudes and latitudes — partly culled from predecessors, partly determined by himself. However, many were deduced from measured distances rather than astronomical observations; furthermore, he used a value for the Earth's circumference which was much smaller than Eratosthenes' relatively accurate result. This led to an estimated transatlantic distance between Europe and Asia which was far too small — something which appears to have encouraged Columbus in his decision to try to reach Asia by crossing the Atlantic. An error by Ptolemy may therefore have led Renaissance Europe to rediscover America at a comparatively early date.

Alexandria became, in addition, a centre of instrumental and engineering science. A water clock with mechanical action was perfected by *Ctesibos* (a third century BC Alexandrian barber and engineer) and by *Philo of Byzantium*, a second century military engineer employed by Alexandria. Much later (first to second centuries AD) came *Hero of Alexandria*, who invented the first steam-driven engine. This was a reaction turbine consisting of a spherical chamber out of which steam escaped from oppositely angled, diametrically opposed nozzles; it spun about a fixed axis — a kind of spherical catherine wheel. Hero discovered the law of reflection of light, showing that the angles of incidence and reflection of a light beam on a mirror were equal. A versatile man, he also did some original work in geometry and surveying.

Singular advances were made at the Museum in physiology. In the third century BC, a systematic survey of the whole human body was undertaken. Many new facts were ascertained concerning the structure of the human brain, of the nervous and circulatory systems. The difference between arteries and veins was established. Some of this knowledge, one fears, was obtained at the cost of *human* vivisection (Herophilos of Chalcedon and Erasistratos of Iulis, third century BC). Later, of course, there was the famous contemporary of Ptolemy: *Galen of Pergamum* (AD 130-200) who spent some time in Alexandria, but eventually settled in Rome. Many regard him as the father of modern physiology and as a physician second only to Hippocrates in his influence on the course of Western medicine.

Hellenistic science raises many interesting questions. One may, for instance, contemplate the fact that Alexandrian scientists failed to accept a heliocentric model for the solar system. Aristarchos' bold hypothesis had been endorsed by Seleucos the Babylonian and Apollonius' treatise on conics had, after all, supplied the necessary theoretical ingredients. An important obstacle, certainly, was the shiboleth of circular motion which, originating with Pythagoras, had been upheld by Plato and Aristotle; the ancients still loomed close and their authority, even in Alexandria, was formidable. Yet the scientists of the day questioned their elders' judgments, or science would have stood still: Theophrastos, Straton and others explicitly rejected Aristotle's views on final causes, Aristarchos rejected the geocentric credo, the atomists rejected Aristotle's ruling on the non-existence of a vacuum. More was involved, clearly, than simple mind-set.

A major difficulty lay in the absence of adequate data. Existing astronomical tables were neither detailed nor accurate enough for Alexandrian astronomers to have discovered Kepler's laws of planetary motion. One cannot help feeling that they could have remedied this problem by improving their instruments: fifteen hundred years later Tycho de Brahe merely used larger, more accurate versions of the same pre-telescopic instruments to obtain the data Kepler was to need. And here was the rub: on the whole, Greek interest in refining their instruments seems to have been lukewarm.

This relative lack of enthusiasm for the practical side of science is curious for, when pressed, the Greeks were excellent and careful observers — witness Hipparchos' remarkable discovery of the precession of the equinoxes, or Eratosthenes measurement of the Earth's circumference. The truth may be that they were inhibited by social attitudes: contempt for craft work will hardly breed an understanding of what it can do for knowledge. Certainly, in the hands of men like Archimedes or Hero who straddled the fields of mathematics and engineering, science came close to breaking down the barriers between theory and experiment. Nevertheless one recalls Xenophon's comments on the *social stigma* attached to the *mechanical arts* and, five centuries later, Plutarch's paraphrasing of Archimedes on the *ignoble and sordid business of mechanics*; the prejudice against craft work was deep and persistent. In astronomy, to be sure, Athenian and Alexandrian philosphers strove valiantly to *save the phenomena*; in biology and anatomy they described nature's workings with painstaking care; in geodesy they measured the Earth. Yet all this is not the same as designing laboratory experiments — and tools — to test an idea or a theory, or to answer specific questions.

The reluctance of the Greeks to do experimental work mirrored their contempt for manual labour. A factor here was their slave economy: they had little reason to be interested in labour-saving devices. Their technology and their instrumentation remained primitive, they did few experiments and this not only kept them from developing modern astronomical models, it also prevented their whole science from evolving. This is particularly obvious in their physics. Our universe is dynamic; a crucial link between mathematical description — modelling — and the actual behaviour of things (arrows, stones or planets) is the understanding of how force produces motion. This could never be achieved without the kind of perceptive, imaginative experimentation carried out fifteen hundred years later by Galileo, and so the Greeks never developed a proper science of dynamics. They were, above all, superb mathematicians; wherever observation and geometry were sufficient to establish the facts, they usually came to the right conclusions. But when progress required the development of new instrumental and experimental techniques, their success appears to have been erratic. However, one must be careful with such generalizations; the development of science is an extraordinarily complex, poorly understood process — one is ever in danger of oversimplifying.

It remains true, nevertheless, that the Greek commitment was to knowledge, not tools. Mathematics and philosophy were central to their picture of the world. Scientists like Pythagoras and Aristotle were also philosophers, and philosophers like Democritos and Plato had an effect upon the course of science. *Pure* science and philosophy walked hand in hand and were, for the Greeks, superior to other forms of knowledge. This dampened their enthusiasm for experiment and may have retarded their science. Nevertheless their achievements were stupendous. More than twenty-three centuries have elapsed since the days of Pythagoras, Aristotle, Archimedes and Euclid yet these are still household names; much of what they discovered remains securely part of our culture. Archimedes' principle and Euclid's *Elements* are still taught yearly to millions of reluctant schoolchildren. Without the benefit of sophisticated instruments or techniques Eratosthenes measured the Earth's circumference to within almost one per cent and Hipparchos discovered the precession of the equinoxes. Aristarchos proposed the heliocentric model of the solar system seventeen centuries before Copernicus. Theophrastos wrote the first treatise on geology. Hippocrates founded medicine as our civilization defines it. Hero of Alexandria invented the first steam-driven machinery. The Greeks laid the foundation of modern mathematics; they discovered irrational numbers, conic sections and the properties of many curves. Two thousand years before it could be properly demonstrated, Democritos divined the atomic nature of matter and Epicuros guessed its randomness. Seen from any kind of perspective these achievements, telescoped into a mere few centuries, look miraculous.

The waning of Hellenistic science coincided, to a considerable degree, with the growth of the Roman Empire — Archimedes' death at the hands of a Roman soldier seems symbolic. The Romans themselves contributed nothing new or original to science: they were fine engineers but indifferent scientists. Nevertheless, cultured Romans respected the achievements of the Greeks: a number of discussions and compilations of Greek science were written in Latin. The poet *Lucretius* (first century BC) composed *On the Nature of Things (De Rerum Natura)* — a didactic poem containing an account of atomism and the teachings of Epicuros. *Pliny the Elder* (first century AD) wrote his *Historiae Naturalis* — a collection of fact and phantasy summarizing extant zoological knowledge, and one of the principal natural history sources for the Dark Ages. The Museum of Alexandria continued to function as the world's chief scientific centre. With Hero and Ptolemy it had a period of renascence. Thereafter its brilliance faded.

By the fifth century AD the Roman Empire in the West was falling apart under the pressure of barbarian hordes. Science in the Mediterranean was being driven East by a Christian theocracy hostile to secular knowledge. Diodorus, Bishop of Tarsus (fourth century AD) declared Greek cosmology to be atheistic. Towards the end of the fourth century the great Alexandrian Library was burned down and most of its priceless treasures destroyed. In the year 415 *Hypatia*, daughter of Theon and the last mathematician of Alexandria, was savagely murdered by a Christian mob insti-gated, it is said, by the Patriarch Cyril. In one of his most purple passages, Gibbon describes her as

> torn from her chariot, stripped naked, dragged to the church, and inhumanly butchered by the hands of Peter the Reader and a troop of savage and merciless fanatics: her flesh was scraped from her bones with sharp oyster-shells and her quivering limbs were delivered to the flames.[3]

In 529 the Christian Emperor Justinian closed the schools of Athens — which, despite two centuries of officially sanc-tioned hostility, were still attempting to dispense a modi-cum of enlightenment. Knowledge retrogressed; whereas the ancients, from Pythagoras to Ptolemy had known the Earth to be a sphere and had measured its dimensions, the early fathers of the church ruled it to be rectangular, slanting and shaped like the Holy Tabernacle. The Western world was engulfed by new centuries of obscurantism, during which scientific prog-ress almost came to a halt.

The teachings of *Augustine* (354-430) crystallized Christian orthodoxy for future centuries, adopting the basically Platonist view on the supremacy of mind and soul. The material world, he asserted, is but shadows; truth is found in the activities of the mind and not in the properties of a transient external world. The only worthwhile knowledge concerns man's rela-tion to God. In his *Soliloquies*, he has the following dialogue with Reason:

> *Reason*: What then do you wish to know? *Augustine*: All these things I have prayed for. *Reason*: Sum them up briefly. *Augustine*:

> God and the soul I desire to know. *Reason*: Nothing more?
> *Augustine*: Nothing whatever. . .[4]

Thus did a tired, otherworldly society embrace a fundamentally anti-science, anti-intellectual philosophy.

Yet during the ensuing age of darkness the spark of science continued to flicker, here and there, flaring occasionally to produce some remarkable insight — buried, usually, and all but invisible in endless theological meanderings. Thus the interesting case of *John Philoponus* — *the Grammarian* — who worked in Alexandria in the first half of the sixth century. A convert to Christianity, much of his work is an effort to fuse Aristotelian and Christian views. Hidden in his writings — described by Sarton as repellingly prolix — are the first adumbrations of modern mechanical principles. Philoponus argued that a force transferred *impetus* — a kind of inner moving force — to a body. This was the forerunner of our concepts of momentum and inertia: impetus kept the body going after the original force was removed. There was no need for an external mover, no need for air to fill the space behind the flying arrow to push it on its way — no need for prime movers or angelic beings to propel the heavenly bodies. This was a major intellectual breakthrough — the seed of the mechanics of Galileo and Newton.[1] The fortunes of this concept during the next thousand years were to be mixed. It was revolutionary — and Philoponus was duly convicted of heresy.[5,6]

The earliest mathematics, the first science, had come from Sumer, Babylon and Egypt, reaching fertile soil in Ionia, diffusing westwards to Greece, Sicily and North Africa. Now, under the pressure of Christian intolerance, it flowed back, eastward, where it was welcomed, preserved and sometimes bettered by a young and vigorous Muslim culture. Fine work was done in Baghdad where, under the Caliphs, important progress was achieved in algebra. There was the great encyclopaedist *al-Biruni* (973-1048) who observed that the speed of light far exceeded that of sound. A new insight, coming from India and

---

[1]According to N.G. Wilson some scholars have suggested that Philoponus 'appears to be of greater originality than he really was because of a failure to name his sources . . .' [Scholars of Byzantium, Duckworth 1983, p. 45]

eventually reaching us, appeared then in the Arab world: this was the concept of the *zero*, an abstraction and notation without which modern mathematics and much of science would be very awkward, if not impossible. A large segment of Greek thought was translated and preserved by the Arabs; some was systematized and improved upon. The alchemists were active through these times, but their contribution to science is hard to assess.

One must wait until the waning of the Middle Ages to see the flow of knowledge change direction once more and turn westwards to bring life, again, to Western science and philosophy.

CHAPTER SEVEN

Transition

At a point halfway between the villages of Galphay and Studley in North Yorkshire, the Laver has cut itself a steep-sided, peaceful little valley which, though it is only a few miles from these and other villages, has a strange quality of remoteness. Perhaps the woods make it so, or perhaps it is the sound of running water, but here one feels removed from daily cares, shut off from the world's bustle and tensions. There is in this valley a small, ancient bridge; wild garlic grows on it, nettles and brambles cover it in rich, living profusion. A beech, pushing through one corner, has damaged it, nudging aside the old stones and opening a crack in the dry walls; other trees grow close by and they too have sent out roots, plucking at the structure. It spans a tiny tributary of the Laver, almost hidden by the vegetation; walking through the dense undergrowth, it is easily missed. To see it best one must come here on a sunny day, when shards of light, filtering through the high canopy of beech and fir, help pick out the green mossy stones of a small arch, a bare three feet above the hurrying water, under which the stream bed has been carefully paved with slivers of pale sandstone; time has smoothed these and rounded their edges, yet they still work as intended: the water slips quickly and cleanly over the little race.

Clearly, this structure is very old. The land once belonged to the Fountains Abbey Priory; in all likelihood, the bridge has stood here for five or six hundred years, perhaps more. Built by Cistercian monks in the Middle Ages it has, through centuries of war and social upheaval, stood quietly in this woodland corner, survived the sack of the Abbey, attacked only by vegetation and the forces of nature. The monks who built it did their job well; without mortar they made a solid arch which, even when pushed and jostled by the roots of several great trees, has refused to collapse. There is something comforting about these enduring, tangible links with the past; they offer the kind of history that does not delude and is not found in books — a simple truth one can reach out and touch. This ancient bridge, lost in a small wooded Yorkshire valley, mute attestation to past craftsmanship and honest work, is also a sample of the medieval know-how which could be mustered to solve some immediate problem, like taking a road across a stream.

Throughout Europe and the British Isles various technologies had, during the Middle Ages, made slow but significant progress. The Romans too had known how to handle stone and had built great aqueducts and roads; but medieval Europe invented the flying buttress and bequeathed us its cathedrals. The Mediterranean peoples had used the iron plough since 1000 BC; in the tenth and eleventh centuries AD the feudal farmer learnt how to draw it with horses. The fortified villages of the Dark Ages turned into towns; within their walls shopkeepers and tradespeople prospered in times of plenty, and a middle-class bourgeoisie was born; monasteries grew rich. The improved methods of farming, allied to the new technology of watermills and, eventually, of windmills (twelfth century) led to increased production and occasionally to food surpluses and wealth (a contributory factor here were low population figures — kept low, in particular, by wars and plague). This, it has been said, led to new kinds of enterprise — from crusading to cathedral building and scholarship. Safer, more controlled sea travel and commerce became possible with the invention in China of the sternpost rudder, fore-and-aft rigs and the marine compass. From China, too, came papermaking and movable block printing [woodblock printing appeared in Europe in the twelfth century — leading eventually to the perfecting of movable metal print by Gutenberg in Mainz (1448)]. Gunpowder was invented in the eleventh century, also in China, reaching Europe in the thirteenth. Crafts specialized and prospered; a new category of literate instrument makers came into being, people who banded into guilds and left notebooks and systematized their techniques. The first mechanical clocks were seen on thirteenth century cathedrals and in public places; pocket watches appeared in Nuremberg in the sixteenth.

In the centuries spanning the waning of the Middle Ages and

the Renaissance, science and philosophy underwent radical changes; there was, in fact, a *Scientific Revolution*. Was it the inevitable result of a natural evolution of ideas? Was it triggered primarily by social and economic factors? How important was the role of individual thinkers? Many answers to these questions have been adduced — answers coloured, inevitably, by the particular interests or bias of their authors. The historian Herbert Butterfield lays stress on the emergence of Western Europe to a position of relative stability and cultural leadership, thanks at least in part to the containment of Turkish and Mongol hordes to the East. Bernal insists on the primacy of economic and social pressures. It seems reasonable to assume also that the rise of technology and crafts must have stimulated interest in practical knowledge — and thereby encouraged natural philosophers to use tools, experiment and observe. The knowledge-power relationship was coming into its own. And there was another ingredient: the intellectual ferment was seeded, and the seed came from the Arab world.

While in Christian Europe intellectual originality had been at a low ebb, Islamic culture — whose empire extended from India to Spain — had risen to great heights. The flowering of Islam in the tenth and eleventh centuries preceded and engendered the rebirth of European science. In the Near East (Syria, Persia) Islam had accumulated and translated into Arabic a rich repository of classical literature — a great storehouse of Greek science and philosophy. In the Far East it had absorbed new knowledge in mathematics, alchemy and medicine, and had also made advances of its own. It had kept going the astronomical observations of the Chaldeans — which now extended uninterrupted over three millennia, a treasure for both Moslem and future Christian astronomers. Comparing tenth and eleventh century European science to that of Islam, said Sarton, is 'almost like passing from the shade to the open sun and from a sleepy world into one tremendously active'.[1]

Much of Islamic science, to be sure, was derivative — synthetic and encyclopaedic, gathering into itself all available sources of knowledge. Its physics was Aristotelian and its universe was Ptolemy's (whose *Syntaxis* bore in translation the title of *the Almagest*). Yet its mathematicians, like *Omar Khayyam* (1038-1123), were amongst the greatest of the Middle

Ages. Many of its great men, such as the Persians *al Biruni* (973-1048) and *Ibn Sina* or Avicenna (980-1037) were not only encyclopaedists but also very original thinkers and polymaths — astronomers, doctors, mathematicians, geologists, philosophers and alchemists.

There was in Islam mounting discontent with the Ptolemaic model of the heavens: no honest observer could help seeing the growing discrepancies between its predictions and actual measurements of star and planet positions through the years. In the second half of the twelfth century *al Bitruji* (Alpetragius) revived, in modified form, the Aristotelian cosmology of homocentric spheres. He assumed a Prime Mover for the ninth sphere and introduced additional motions for the inner spheres: contemporary Hebrew scholars named him *ha-marish* — he who causes the heavens to vacillate. This new *Alpetragian* model caused a stir and vied for a while with Ptolemy's, until it became clear that it was no improvement over its predecessor. Of special significance for the evolution of Western science was the Egyptian *Ibn al Haithan* or *al Hazen* (965-1039). His emphasis on experimental work was taken to heart by later Christian men of science such as Grosseteste and Roger Bacon. His treatise on optics, dealing with mirrors, lenses and spherical aberrations, was to remain a standard work for centuries and would influence Roger Bacon and Kepler.

Of the Islamic philosophers who crowned the culture of this period, the most important is *Ibn Rushd* or *Averroes* (1126-98), whose interpretation of Aristotle was tremendously influential for medieval Christian science and philosophy. Averroes' brand of Aristotelianism was distinguished by a number of controversial features. One, significant from a theological standpoint but of little scientific consequence, was the denial of personal immortality. Another, of real import to the evolution of science in a clergy-dominated society, was the doctrine of the *two truths* which maintained that what is true on one level (philosophy, science) need not be so on another (theology). This sanctioned lines of thought outside the boundaries of orthodoxy: empirical and sensory evidence relating to the physical universe could be allowed to contradict the *a priori* pronouncements of the theologians. This, of course, was to the taste of neither the Moslem nor the Christian hierarchies.

Averroism was attacked both by fundamentalist Moslems and, later, by the Christian Church which branded it as a dangerous heresy. Nevertheless, while it was stamped out in Islam, it survived in Europe where it rekindled interest in the empirical content of Aristotle and of science in general. For a while it attracted the interest of the Franciscan order and flourished at the universities of Paris and Padua (fourteenth and fifteenth centuries). Averroism shook Christian orthodoxy and encouraged the acceptance of a new experimental spirit. Averroes, then, should be seen as a vital figure in the history of Western scientific thought.

The glory that was Islam in the tenth, eleventh and twelfth centuries suffered the fate of so many other high cultures. Like the Egyptians at the dawn of history, like the Classical culture at the beginning of our own Dark Age, it succumbed to religious orthodoxy and obscurantism. Stifled by the Imams, Islamic science began its decline in the twelfth century and was largely stagnant by the fourteenth. Meanwhile Christian European scholarship was coming alive. Some historians see the twelfth century as a crossover — intellectual supremacy passing from the Moslems to the Europeans. George Sarton has used this simile:

> Let us close our eyes for a moment and try to see things in a very simplified manner, as they would appear from a great distance, in a sort of vision. The stately chariot which carries the highest hopes and the noblest thoughts of mankind has been stopped to change horses in the neighbourhood of an inn. The old Muslim postillons are being thanked and new ones are taking charge. The chariot is stopped, but the fresh horses are pawing the ground impatiently. A last glass to the driver and the barmaid bids him Godspeed. In a moment they will be gone. It is the same old chariot, but the horses and postillions are changed from time to time, and the people riding in it change too, one by one . . . But, mark this, *it is a chariot that never comes back*. It goes on and on as the spirit of mankind moves it; it has been driven by Greeks, by Romans, by people of all kinds, lately by Muslims, now by Jews and Christians. Nor does it matter who drives it if it goes safely forward in the right direction.[2]

To be more specific, a salient date for medieval European

scholarship is 1085 — the year in which the Western Crusaders took Toledo. A treasure-trove of Classical science (mostly in Arabic) and of original Moslem work became available to Christian scholars; there followed a long and fruitful era of translation (from Arabic to Latin and, to a lesser extent, into Hebrew). Many of the translators were churchmen (Peter the Venerable, Robert of Chester, Domingo Guadisalvo). Gerard of Cremona (1114-87), perhaps the most famous, was a free-lancer; he headed a Toledo school which translated much of Archimedes, Euclid, Apollonius and the Almagest. In Sicily a translation of Ptolemy was made directly from the Greek around 1160. Valuable Greek manuscripts had also been preserved in Byzantium, and became more commonly available to the West after the capture of Constantinople in 1204 by the armies of the Fourth Crusade. The bulk of the early translating work, however, went into Arabic texts. Europe's Latin-speaking and Hebrew scholars acquainted themselves with a large body of Classical work, together with important Moslem advances in mathematics, astronomy, alchemy, medicine and philosophy. Assimilation of this knowledge was fairly slow. The original texts were often difficult (Aristotle!); Latin renderings of Arabic versions of the Greek, or of Syriac translations thereof, must have generated a fair amount of gibberish which had to be winnowed out. Europe, in other words, was not suddenly flooded with imported Classical and Moslem wisdom. The precious knowledge seeped in gradually, taking a century or more to be assimilated by Christian thinkers.

Another crucial step in the intellectual history of late medieval Europe was the appearance of the universities in Padua, Bologna, Paris, Oxford towards the end of the twelfth and the beginning of the thirteenth centuries. Harbouring scholars of an independent turn of mind, a kind of avant-garde interested in Averroism, experimental science and its implications, they would be called upon, during the following centuries, to play a central role in the development of scientific ideas.

By the beginning of the thirteenth century, the science of Christian Europe was stirring powerfully. Among its earliest important figures was the Dominican *Jordanus Nemorarius* (Teutonicus); his dates are unknown, but he died *c.* 1237. His axiom 'that which can lift a certain weight up to a certain height, can also lift a weight k times heavier to a height k times smaller' comes close to defining what we would now call the potential energy in a gravity field. Jordanus also did careful work on the geometry of motion (kinematics); in discussing the mechanics of moving bodies he drew the distinction, revolutionary in his day, between the total force of gravity and its component along the body's path. He also wrote a number of mathematical treatises. A scholar of renown, he was the Dominican order's second master general. He died during his return from a pilgrimage to the Holy Land.

Another outstanding personage, perhaps the first European with modern views on natural philosophy, was *Robert Grosseteste* (1175-1253). Also known as Robert Greathead, or Robert of Lincoln, he was famed as a theologian and a teacher. We may also see him as a physicist, philosopher, astronomer and mathematician. The image of the man is blurred but we know he was, at various times, Bishop of Lincoln, first Chancellor of Oxford University, lecturer to the Oxford Franciscans. Erudite and gifted, he was also a man of principle and moral courage: he did not hesitate to criticise the Roman Curia and he saved Jews from being massacred. His insight into 'the way by which the abstracted universal is reached from the singulars through the help of the senses' (*induction*) and his insistence on the importance of observation — views he imparted to his students — give him a place of honour in the history of Western science. Since he saw clearly how, through 'the rules and principles and fundaments . . . given by the power of geometry, the careful observer of natural things can give the cause of all natural effects' he foreshadowed modern ways. Grosseteste's views on the nature and limitations of scientific knowledge were sophisticated and subtle. He understood, for example, that science does not uniquely relate cause and effect — that the same effect can be produced by more than one set of causes. Much of his thinking comes to us in the form of commentaries on Aristotle's *Physics* or his *Posterior Analytics* and is, in this sense, derivative.[3] But he was the first European to appreciate and re-introduce Aristotelian induction into the pursuit of science.

These thirteenth century adumbrations of Western science were paralleled by interesting philosophical developments. Of special importance was the fact that most of Aristotle became available in Latin. This was to have long-lasting, traumatic effects on theology, philosophy and science. The first reaction of the Christian Church to Aristotle was hostile. His empiricism was disturbing to theologians raised on a diet of Augustinian mysticism; he appeared to contradict too many Christian articles of faith (like that of personal immortality). By 1210 the teaching of Aristotle's natural science was forbidden in Paris; other interdicts followed. But the factual content in his writings was formidable and, to the enlightened, it was clear that accommodations would have to be made. By the middle of the thirteenth century, progressive theologians like *Albertus Magnus* (1206-80) and his pupil *Thomas Aquinas* (1225-74) were studying and expounding Aristotle.

Thomas Aquinas, scion of a noble Italian family, a Dominican from the age of nineteen, devoted his life to the arduous task of reconciling Christianity with Aristotelianism — and to eradicating the latter's less acceptable interpretations, such as Averroism. He succeeded so well that he is still regarded today, with Aristotle, as the Catholic philosopher *par excellence*: well into our century Roman Catholic philosophy remained essentially Thomist. Aquinas' influence on the late Middle Ages was profound. He established a new orthodoxy, competing with and eventually supplanting Augustinian Platonicism — replacing, in effect, one dogma by another. While this was an intellectually impressive feat, most scientists and, I think, most philosophers will concur that his contribution to scientific thought was negligible — or even negative; indeed any philosophy that establishes an orthodoxy must *ipso facto* have a retarding effect on independent thought. But whether Thomism was any more inimical to the progress of science than the Augustinian orthodoxy it replaced is a moot point.

The prevalent Christian philosophy of the late Middle Ages was a kind of sterile Aristotelian scholasticism. Typical of its mode of reasoning are Aquinas' five proofs of the existence of God. A representative sample, derived from Aristotle, is the first — *the argument from motion*:[4]

. . . whatever is moved must be moved by another. If that by which it is moved by itself moved, then this also must needs be moved by another, and that by another again. But this cannot go on to infinity, because then there would be no first mover, and consequently, no other mover, seeing that subsequent movers move only inasmuch as they are moved by the first mover; as the staff moves only because it is moved by the hand. Therefore it is necessary to arrive at a first mover, moved by no other; and this everyone understands to be God.

Many of scholasticism's *'vast, frozen triumphs of logic'*[4] were constructed along such lines. To the modern mind they seem puerile — little better than the Platonicism of Augustine. Nevertheless, theologians of the Middle Ages on the whole saw Aquinas' work as a great achievement. Having reconciled the wisdom of the ancient Greeks with that of the Church Fathers, he appeared to have removed many difficult questions raised by empirical knowledge. Aristotle's final cause was God's will, his Prime Mover was God himself and the inner celestial spheres were propelled by God's angels. All seemed well with the medieval cosmos.

It is difficult for us to reconstruct the spirit of a time so remote, and in some ways so alien. We see it only, to paraphrase Barbara Tuchman, through a distant mirror. It is clear, nonetheless, that apart from the stranglehold of the Church, the environment of the Middle Ages did not encourage independent, original thinking. The Dutch historian, J. Huizinga, had this to say[5]:

> The mentality of the declining Middle Ages often seems to us to display an incredible superficiality and feebleness . . . it proceeds to generalizations unhesitatingly on the strength of a single instance . . . inexactitude, credulity, levity, inconsistency are common features of medieval reasoning. All these defects are rooted in its fundamental formalism.

Such a milieu, one would think, could hardly be conducive to the growth of science. Independent-minded, scientifically inclined philosophers of the thirteenth, fourteenth or fifteenth centuries must have felt desperate, vulnerable and very much alone. Yet the remarkable fact is that, during the waning of the Middle Ages, much progress was made in the sciences.

Some advances still had characteristically medieval motives. Thus the astronomers of Christian Europe, like their Moslem predecessors, were dissatisfied with Ptolemy's model. The reasons for their discontent were religious, calendrical and, most importantly, astrological. Imprecise ephemerides, it was held, led to inaccurate horoscopes. And so astronomical measurements and instrumentation made progress during the Middle Ages in order that the Church could improve its calendars and astrologers make better horoscopes. What fuelled a revived interest in mechanics and physics is less clear. Perhaps the example of Aristotle's empiricism, or the teachings of Averroes, were taking effect. Perhaps practical technology, stirring the drive for power, was having an impact on the world of scholars. Whatever the reasons, following Grosseteste, a series of remarkable thinkers appeared in the second half of the thirteenth century. All appear to have been critical of Thomism.

There was *Peter Olivi* (d. 1298), a French Franciscan who embraced Philoponus' impetus theory — the first on record, apparently, to have done so since the seventh century. This theory, the earliest anticipation of the concepts of momentum and inertia, was seminal; it adumbrated the ideas of Galileo, Descartes, and Newton. As Sarton put it, Peter Olivi's premonition of its importance — he called it the *vis formativai* — deserves our deepest respect.[2] Significantly, he opposed Thomism and many of his ideas were censured and his influence curtailed.

More powerful was the figure of *Peter the Stranger* (Pierre de Maricourt, or Peter Peregrinus; the name Peregrinus, or Stranger, was often bestowed upon Crusaders). A Frenchman from Picardy, his life is poorly documented. In 1261 he wrote a treatise on the astrolabe — a device for taking the altitude of heavenly bodies (invented in the second century BC by Hipparchos, it was the main astronomical instrument of the Middle Ages). In 1269, whilst taking part in the siege of Lucera in southern Italy, he wrote a famous *letter* on the magnet to a friend. Entitled *Epistola ad Sygerum de Foucaucourt militem de magnete*, it is a short treatise on magnetism, and has been described as one of the greatest monuments to experimental research in the Middle Ages. The student of magnetism, says Peter, must be 'industrious in manual work'. In the letter are detailed discussions and observations on magnets, techniques for determining the poles of a lodestone and a description of a floating compass with a reference line and a circle divided into degrees. He may have been the first to use a small spherical lodestone or *terrella* and to demonstrate on it the existence of magnetic meridians or lines of force: he seems to have grasped the general character of the Earth's magnetic field. It was an altogether outstanding piece of work. Sadly, little is known about him.

Jean de Jandun (d.1328), canon of Senlis, also contributed to the theory of magnetism. In particular, he tried to reconcile his belief in Aristotelian mechanics, which required a mover and denied action at a distance, with the fact that magnets *do* act on each other or on pieces of iron from a distance. He stipulated that between a magnet and a piece of iron there exists a medium which is gradually altered as the force or *species magnetica* is transmitted step by step (this sounds remarkably like the magnetic field introduced into modern physics by Faraday five hundred years later). Hostile to Thomism, he was an avowed Averroist — indeed, he is thought to have been the leader of the Parisian Averroists during his later years. His writings earned him excommunication in 1327; he died in exile, under the protection of Ludwig of Bavaria.

A complex interplay of philosophy, faith, technique and personalities, a happy hunting ground for scholars, the history of science is a polemicist's paradise. To pick one person at some moment of time and state that his or her contribution was *the* most important is thus unwise. Occasionally, though, a name stands out; there is a fair consensus on the roles of people like Galileo, Newton, Darwin or Einstein. Historians of medieval science tend to focus on *Roger Bacon* (1220-94?) as the principal scientific figure of the Middle Ages.[2,6,7] Yet why not his teacher Grosseteste — or Peter the Stranger, whose claim to originality as an experimental scientist is at least as impressive? Why not al Hazen, who inspired them? What, for that matter, of Averroes whose philosophy loosened the constraints of medieval orthodoxy and superstition? All were essential to the advancement of medieval science. Whether the singling out of Roger Bacon can be upheld on strictly rational grounds, whether this is likely to withstand the test of time and future scholarship, I leave to others. The fact remains that he was an interesting man; he is also a romantic figure, and more is known about him than of most medieval men of science.[6,3]

Born in Somerset, or perhaps Gloucester, c. 1214-20, independently wealthy, he first studied in Oxford, then in Paris where he began his career as a philosopher, lecturing on Aristotle — well before Aquinas' work had made Aristotelianism respectable. An Aristotelian with Neoplatonist leanings, he believed in divine revelation as leading to superior, transcendent truth. In later years he professed a dislike for Aquinas as a 'teacher yet unschooled' whose works were full of 'puerile vanity and voluminous superfluity'. Around 1247 he became seriously interested in science — probably after returning to Oxford and coming under the influence of Grosseteste. For ten years he gave himself to the study of astronomy, optics, mathematics, alchemy and languages, spending substantial sums of his own on instruments and laboratory work. His mind was brilliant, his memory phenomenal and he acquired an encyclopaedic mastery of existing knowledge and of Greek and Moslem thought. The teaching of Grosseteste, the example of Peter the Stranger, and his understanding of al Hazen and Aristotle, led him to discern and advocate the need for experimental work. For the rest of his life, he would preach the pre-eminence of experimental and observational work over mere reasoning (but *after* divine revelation!). He much admired Peter the Stranger, whom he dubbed *dominus experimentorum*. Yet Bacon himself appears to have done relatively little work of this sort. He did, however, carry out remarkable experiments in optics; in particular, he demonstrated the properties of lenses and the uses of paraboloidal and hyperboloidal mirrors for the elimination of spherical aberrations. Somewhat before spectacles first appeared in Italy, he suggested using lenses for improving eyesight, and it is said that he conceived the principle of the telescope. In opposition to his teacher Grosseteste, he held that transmission of light could not take place instantaneously — but then so had Empedocles 1,400 years before him.

Bacon's knowledge of mathematics was limited. Nevertheless he stressed that whereas, apart from revelation, experimentation is the best source of knowledge, it must be supplemented by mathematics to bear fruit. Like Eudoxos and Archimedes, he foresaw the potential of mathematical physics; but he understood better than they did the nature and importance of experimental work. In astronomy he espoused Ptolemy's system — which, he pointed out, gave a better account of the phenomena than the Alpetragian model. In physics his views were those of Nemorarius and Grosseteste, but he also gave thought to the problems of action at a distance raised by magnetism. To these very sound accomplishments and interests, Bacon appended a long list of speculations on propelling boats by mechanical means, flying with mechanically operated wings or heat-filled buoyant copper balloons, — on the grounds of which it is sometimes claimed that he understood the interrelations of science and technology, i.e., the power of knowledge. Be that as it may, it is clear that to his other talents he added that of visionary — which doubtless accounts for his sobriquet of *Doctor Mirabilis.*

In 1257, in ill health, Roger Bacon became a Franciscan. He was soon in trouble with his superiors. However, he had a friend in Pope Clement IV, to whom he tried to sell the idea of a vast project dealing with all knowledge — a kind of Papal Institute for Advanced Studies. This, he said, would be of great value to the welfare of the Church and to the strengthening of the faith. The Pope was interested and commanded Bacon to send him the information in secret from his Franciscan brethren. Bacon set to work and produced, in short order, his *Opus Majus* and several appendages (*Opus Minus, Opus Tertium*) — an encyclopaedia of extant knowledge in the sciences. One's admiration for this accomplishment is enhanced by the fact that he was working under the burden of secrecy — not allowed to explain to his superiors why he had undertaken this immense and, in their eyes, doubtless suspect task. The work was delivered in 1268 — the year of Clement's death. During the interregnum that followed and the reign of Pope Gregory X, the papacy lost interest in the project and Bacon was left to his own devices, and to the dubious mercies of his fellow friars. In 1278 he was condemned for teaching 'suspected novelties' and, according to a Franciscan chronicle, was imprisoned until his death in 1294 (1292?).

Bacon's original research in optics, his speculations, his erudition, his imprisonment, his disrespect for authority, have created about him a legendary aura. He has been pictured as a revolutionary who foresaw modern developments, a visionary and a martyr of science, and father of the experimental approach of modern science. But Bacon must at least share this paternity with Peter the Stranger, who was a greater experimental scientist, and with Grosseteste who taught him; in fact he did few experiments, even if he described many — some feasible, others clearly not. His disrespect for authority was, all too often, of a very personal kind; he was brilliant and far more gifted than the majority of people he came in touch with — a truth he may have taken trouble to emphasise. Most likely Bacon was imprisoned not only for his views, but also for being arrogant and argumentative; as Sarton puts it, he was a *mauvais coucheur* — a kicker and a grouch. There is little doubt that he made his fellow Franciscans suffer; it would take almost a century before the good friars mustered the fervour to place Bacon firmly on their list of great Franciscan natural philosophers.

As a philosopher, Bacon was, in fact, far from revolutionary. His enthusiasm for experimental methods may have given an Averroist tinge to his thinking and made him suspect to his contemporaries. But he accepted the teachings of traditional Christianity and, in particular, the primacy of knowledge obtained through revelation. One may see him as a spokesman for the more advanced natural philosophers of his day — a spokesman of genius, yet a genius divided. His world-view was strictly medieval. Like most contemporary thinkers he pursued knowledge in the service of the Church and for the greater glorification of God. Says he in his *Opus Majus*:

> There is one wisdom that is perfect and this is contained in the
> Scriptures. From the root of this wisdom all truth has sprung.
> I say, therefore, that one science is the mistress of all others,
> namely theology . . . whose nod and authority the rest of the
> sciences obey.

And:

> Just as we see nothing corporeally without corporeal light, so
> it is impossible for us to see anything spiritually without the
> spiritual light of divine grace.

Yet his views on the pursuit of science are modern:

> He therefore who wishes to rejoice without doubt in regard to
> the truths underlying phenomena must know how to devote
> himself to experiment. For authors write many statements, and
> people believe them through reasoning which they formulate
> without experience. Their reasoning is wholly false . . .

It is unclear how Bacon reconciles this with his picture of
theology as a science, let alone 'that one science' which is
'the mistress of all others'.

In the century following Bacon's death much thought was
given to the central questions of mechanics and physics: what
is motion? is there a vacuum? how is force transmitted? The
most interesting thinking here went towards sharpening the
impetus concept. The fourteenth century witnessed a slow
chiselling into shape of the ideas of momentum and inertia
— cornerstones of Galilean and Newtonian mechanics without which there simply could be no physics, and probably
no science, as we understand them today. The people most
instrumental in bringing about this emergence were William of
Ockham, Jean Buridan, Nicole Oresme, Albert of Saxony and
Nicolas of Cusa.

William of Ockham (Occam) (1295-1349), like Bacon, was an
English Franciscan who studied at Oxford. He is famous for
having preached the law of parsimony: *It is vain to do with more
what can be done with fewer* (Occam's razor — a principle which
had surfaced many times before). Ockham took Aquinas' first
proof of the existence of God to be false — pointing to the
existence of action at a distance as demonstrated by magnets, which he assumed, logically enough, would also take

place in a void. Aristotle, he said, had been wrong: space did not have to be filled with matter to transmit motion; not only was a vacuum possible, but an arrow could fly through it. Dubious of Thomism, Ockham insisted on separating faith and reason. Actively hostile to the papacy, he was excommunicated and, like Jean de Jandun before him, found refuge with Ludwig of Bavaria. He died in 1349, probably of the Black Death.

Jean Buridan (d.1358?), a French Occamist, taught similar ideas at the University of Paris, of which he was rector. He is justly famed for modernising Philoponus' old theory, revived shortly before by Olivi, which says that force imparts impetus to a body; it is this which keeps the body moving after the force has been removed. Buridan described impetus as proportional to the density, volume and speed of the body; he thus defined it as *momentum* in the modern sense. This quantity, said Buridan, does not normally decay, unless motion takes place in a resistive medium; thus in his *Quaestiones in Libros Metaphysicae*:

> Many posit that the projectile, after leaving the projector, is moved by an *impetus* given by the projector, and that it is moved as long as the *impetus* remains stronger than the resistance. The *impetus* would last indefinitely if it were not diminished by a resisting contrary, or by an inclination to a contrary motion; and in celestial motion there is no resisting contrary . . .

Buridan, we see, is applying impetus theory to the heavens. This too is a breakthrough: it extends, for the first time in history, our earthly laws of mechanics to the stars. In his work on physics (*Quaestiones Octavi Libri Physicorum*), Buridan puts it this way:

> One does not find in the Bible that there are Intelligences charged to communicate to the celestial spheres their proper motions; it is permissible then to show that it is not necessary to suppose the existence of such Intelligences. One could say, in fact, that God, when he created the Universe, set each of the celestial spheres in motions as it pleased him, impressing on each an *impetus* which has moved it ever since . . . These *impetus* which God impressed on the celestial bodies have not

been reduced or destroyed by the passage of time, because there was not, in celestial bodies, any inclination towards other movements, and there was no resistance which could corrupt or restrain these *impetus*.

Here sounds the death-knoll of Aristotelian physics, and of medieval cosmology with its prime movers and pious angels who kept the celestial spheres in motion. The laws of physics, conceived on earth, are being extended to the universe at large. This is the door to modern times — the beginnings of a path which a small band of fourteenth and fifteenth century thinkers was to follow to its logical conclusions. The way would not be easy; there were too many old preconceptions to slough off; and there was the opposition of the Church — of which Buridan was clearly conscious, for he ends the above paragraph with:

All this I do not give as certain; I would merely ask theologians to teach me how all these things could come about . . .

Expelling the Prime Mover from the heavens was too much like a downgrading of God — it smelled of heresy. Buridan's works were placed on *the Index*. But his students, who were many, spread his teachings far and wide; despite the Church's hostility he became the most influential and important figure in fourteenth century science.

Nicole Oresme (1323-82), Bishop of Lisieux, court scholar and advisor to Charles V the Wise, followed Buridan on the path which was to lead to Galileo and to Newton. His special contribution was to help put the theory of mechanics into viable mathematical form. With several Oxford mathematicians, he established the basic rules for uniformly accelerated motion. Since he also propounded the notion of the earth's rotation and, of course, the theory of impetus, he seems to have been unusually perspicacious. A contemporary, *Albert of Saxony* (1316-90) can also be taken as a forerunner of Galileo, because he maintained that the speed of a falling body was either proportional to the distance fallen or to time — without being able to make up his mind between the two hypotheses. And he made a wonderful geological statement: to compensate the disruption of static equilibrium due to surface erosion by water, he said there had to be a steady uplifting of the continents. He visualized the Earth's history as a cyclic succession of uplifts and erosional episodes.

The fifteenth century did strangely little for the impetus theory; only a minority of scholars supported it. One of the best was *Nicolas of Cusa* (1401-64) who believed both in the rotation of the Earth (occurring by virtue of an impetus given to it at the beginning of time), and in the essential similarity of Earth and the heavenly bodies. Gravitation, he maintained, was a local phenomenon and each star a centre of attraction . . .

Thus, in the philosophical and theological debates of the late Middle Ages, the modern interplay of reason (mathematics) and controlled observation (experiment) began to emerge — in the hands of people like Roger Bacon, Peter the Stranger, Oresme, Buridan and others. Shaking loose from the burden of Aristotelian metaphysics and teleology, combining mathematics and experimentation, natural philosophers began to work with the kind of questions that *could* be answered. There came about a better understanding of the uses of *quantity* as opposed to *quality*. Philosophy and science, handmaidens since the times of Classical Greece, began to drift apart — perhaps to their mutual benefit. Predictably, some practitioners of the new methods became over enthusiastic. Oresme tried to apply the theory of impetus to psychology and *Jacopo da Forli* (d. 1413), a Padua physician, treated health as something to be expressed numerically in degrees. But now, neither excessive enthusiasm nor bad logic could bring progress to a halt. Having grasped the uses of empirical verification and mathematics, the scientific enterprise would henceforth be increasingly able to rectify its own mistakes; in this sense, at least, it was becoming self-correcting. More threatening were external factors and, in particular, the power of the Church.

The Middle Ages was an era of religious faith. For centuries, intellectual life was governed by the Church, which kept a sharp lookout for heresy — for anything that threatened its power over lives and souls. During the Dark Ages — from the sixth to the eleventh centuries — the Church successfully repressed most forms of intellectual originality: Christian Europe produced neither scientific thinkers nor,

with one exception, philosophers of any standing (the exception was *John Scotus Erigena*, an Irishman who lived between 810
and 877 and who defended reason so well that his books were
burned). Yet, given its monopoly of the sources of knowledge
and its power, it is hardly surprising that the intelligent and the
educated gravitated to the Church — it offered security and,
with it, access to Europe's extant literature and knowledge.
Reason and ideas, however, have lives of their own; for sharp
and honest minds heresy is, sooner or later, inevitable. By
drawing so many of the best people into its fold, the Church
itself guaranteed the eventual *internal* erosion of its hold over
men's minds. Of the great names in science during the late
Middle Ages only Peter the Stranger and Buridan were laymen.
Nemorarius, Grosseteste, Jean de Jandun, Oresme, Peter Olivi,
Roger Bacon, William of Ockham were all churchmen; the last
three were Franciscans. All had their troubles with the hierarchy, and some had to flee for their lives; yet all succeeded in
advancing scientific knowledge — and, in the process, under-
mined the rigid orthodoxy of medieval Christianity (without, as
far as one can see, seriously impairing their own faith).

The role of the medieval Church in the growth of science
was therefore distinctly ambivalent. As Whitehead remarked,
it indirectly encouraged the growth of science by fostering the
notion of a rational, personal God — i.e., 'a trust in the order of
Nature'. And, as a haven for scholars, it directly encouraged
the proliferation of new ideas. Yet, at the same time, it made
desperate efforts to keep this knowledge from undermining its
dogma; this was a battle it could not win. Too late, the *auto-da-fés*
of the Inquisition; too late the burning of Giordano Bruno and
the trial of Galileo. By the time of the Reformation, modern
science would emerge from its chrysalis. Hopefully, it seems
as if something in us is too strong for censorship, orthodoxy
or tyranny. Perhaps it is our holy curiosity; or perhaps it is our
thirst for power; most likely it is a mixture of both.

CHAPTER EIGHT

Rebirth

For those who like their history in stone, few sights are more splendid than Fountains Abbey on a late summer afternoon, when the cavernous eyes of the Norman arcades are dark with shadow and the sun's last rays turn the gritstone walls to gold. Poignant reminders of the ephemeral quality of all our works, the great Cistercian abbeys of Yorkshire — Rievaulx, Fountains, Jervaulx — were begun early in the twelfth century, a hundred years before Aquinas, when Averroes was still a child. They started as plain monasteries, constructed of local stone by monks committed to the saving of souls, looking for a simple life and a return to the roots of Christianity. But change was not long in coming. Monks and abbots became more worldly; the spiritual innocence of the Middle Ages began to crumble. Through the thirteenth, fourteenth and fifteenth centuries the Abbeys prospered, acquiring land, turning into large establishments with handsome churches, chapels, cloisters, cellars, kitchens, breweries, guesthouses and even prisons. They earned a reputation for hospitality, fine foods and worldly comforts having little in common with the goals of their founders. In the fifteenth century Abbot Huby built Fountains' splendid tower — against the rules of the order, which forbade the erection of high buildings. He rode about in his own private coach and, it is said, thought nothing of entertaining friends with 'a quarter yard of roast beef and a black jack of strong drink'.[1] Today grass and wildflowers grow on the rims of massive walls which once supported heavy timbers and leaded roofing. Open to the winter winds, rain and sleet, the chapels, cloisters and sacristies are now silent; though legend has it that sometimes, on still evenings, one hears faint ghostly snatches of medieval plainsong.

119

To some extent the great Abbeys brought the Dissolution of the Monasteries (1530-40) upon themselves: they became too rich — irresistible prizes for a greedy monarch. By 1530 or so the monastic orders owned roughly ten per cent of all English land; according to Cromwell's *Valor Ecclesiasticus* their yearly income was over £160,000 — a huge sum, considering that one could live, modestly, on £5 a year.[2] A growing laxity played into their enemies' hands, engendering moral support for Henry VIII's plunder. The Abbeys were appropriated by the Crown and their lands sold. Pillaged of their treasures, their lead roofing melted down, their very stones were pilfered and used for buildings elsewhere. Yet the ruins of Fountains Abbey stand for more than an exercise in looting. Henry's reign was a time of religious and political turmoil, of complex histori-cal cross-currents and shifting philosophies; a Cistercian ruin conveys different messages to different people. One thing is clear, however: the Dissolution was a period of cataclysmic change, during which a whole way of life disappeared forever. These broken walls and crumbling arches reflect a revolution, a philosophical, humanistic and artistic upheaval which swept across the face of Europe and the British Isles, and transfigured society.

It is customary to distinguish two main strands in this revolu-tion connected to, or at least paralleling, profound changes in science: the *Reformation*, which was primarily religious, and the *Renaissance*, which was essentially secular.

The Reformation began as a reaction against the corruption of the Church. It signalled the birth of a new view of humanity's relationship to God. People, said Luther, should find their truth in the Bible; protestants substituted its authority for that of the Church. Salvation was to be found by the individual in faith, not in the Church. It was a return to primitive Christianity and, more significantly, an affirmation of man's independence from authority.

The Renaissance was, in some ways, the secular concomi-tant of this new independence. In politics nationalism and sovereignty replaced and opposed ecclesiastical authority. Money and capital became dominant economic factors; the self-made man appeared upon the scene. The working philoso-phy of this *new man* was a pragmatic, at times cynical *humanism* of the kind described by Machiavelli (the *Christian* humanists, on the other hand, whose spokesman was Erasmus, sought to reform the Church without siding with the Lutherans). There was, in all layers of society, great interest in the new — in the novel ideas of philosophy and science, in exploration, in technology, in fresh approaches to painting and music. In every field there occurred changes, *many* revolutions which, in one way or another, were all connected. The increasing willingness to question and explore, the expanding geographical and economic frontiers, realism and perspective in the arts, were all part of the tides of change. The Renaissance and the Reformation are an interweaving of many strands, of action and reaction, a vast tapestry that must be seen as a whole.

Deep transformations in the sciences during the late Middle Ages and the Renaissance are visible enough, yet it is impossible to ascribe to them simple, unambiguous causes. Even to pin them down in time is not easy. The intellectual revolution leading to modern science seems to begin with the waning of the Middle Ages, when Grosseteste, Roger Bacon, Peter Peregrinus first talked seriously of experimental work. Science entered the modern age with Galileo. By the end of the seventeenth century, with Newton, the Western scientific Leviathan had begun its progress. Gestation and birth had taken several centuries; to claim that modern science appeared during the Renaissance or the Reformation would be absurd. But it is true that, in the century between Copernicus' *De Revolutionibus* (1542) and Galileo's *Dialogues*, (1636) critical changes took place.

Foremost was the shift in attitudes characteristic of both Reformation and Renaissance, which led to the rejection of authority. Buridan and Oresme, already, had been disenchanted with Thomism and Aristotle. By the early seventeenth century, one finds Galileo rejecting them openly. This overthrow of the ancients went hand-in-hand with the abandonment of teleological arguments. Medieval science had been teleological in the sacerdotal sense — everything in it was subservient to a Divine Purpose. Aristotelian science, in its insistence on the importance of final causes, had also been teleological — in a secular sense. The two had to some extent been fused in Thomism. During the Renaissance all this was swept aside. Some preconceptions ingrained through the centuries lingered. Strands of Aristotelian thought, like the *horror vacui*, hung on for a while. But the Renaissance was the time when such ideas began to be rejected systematically and consciously. It was a turning point.

The rejection of authority, the willingness to question, came with the birth of a true empirical spirit — which took on its modern form with Galileo, four centuries after its awakening in the minds of Grosseteste, Roger Bacon and Peter Peregrinus. A slow process, it could not be hurried. A hundred years before Galileo, Leonardo da Vinci (1452-1519) expressed it thus:

> All our knowledge has its origins in our perceptions.

> But before you found a law . . . test it two or three times and see whether the experiments produce the same effects.

> Anyone who in discussion relies upon authority uses, not his understanding, but rather his memory . . .

With new attitudes, came new knowledge — from the work of many great figures. There was, for instance, Paracelsus — Aureolus Philippus Theophrastus Bombastus von Hohenheim (1493-1543) — who, in his effort to conjoin the ancient arts of medicine and alchemy founded iatrochemistry, suggesting that for each illness there must be a specific chemical cure. A flamboyant character, he demonstrated his rejection of ancient authority by publicly burning a treatise by Avicenna. Leonardo's exquisite anatomical drawings and Vesalius' (1514-64) *De Humani Corporis Fabrica* represented considerable advances in the field of physiology. And early in the seventeenth century William Harvey (1578-1657), through careful experimentation, demonstrated that blood circulates in veins and arteries according to the principles of hydraulics.

The empirical, experimental spirit was growing everywhere. In this the role of crafts, with their practical insights, was vital. Robert Norman, a compass-maker and retired mariner, established that magnetism was a purely orienting force: a floating magnet would turn and orient itself on a north-south line, but would not move forwards. He is credited by some to have also discovered the dip of the Earth's magnetic field — the fact that a freely suspended compass needle, while assuming a north-south direction would also point at a downward angle. He published his results in a pamphlet entitled *The Newe Attraction* (1581).

The lessons of craftsmanship were combined with scholarship and theoretical curiosity in *William Gilbert of Colchester* (1544-1603). Born a year after Copernicus' death, educated first at Cambridge and perhaps also at Oxford, he studied medicine in Italy and, in the latter part of his life, became physician to Queen Elizabeth. He carried out serious and careful experiments on magnetism. His sympathy for experimental work was doubtless a reflection of the growing awareness of the practical uses of scientific knowledge. It was, after all, the age of ocean exploration, of the colonization of the New World, of great mercantile voyages. Improvement of the compass, understanding of the Earth's magnetism, the determination of latitudes, represented the kind of knowledge that made fortunes and saved lives. And so, following Robert Norman, Gilbert invested much effort in measuring the dip of the compass needle; following Peter the Stranger, he studied small lodestone spheres or *terellas*, and showed the Earth itself to be an immense magnet whose poles were close to the geographic ones. In *On the Lodestone and Magnetic Bodies*, his condemnation of scholasticism and speculation unsubstantiated by experiment is explicit and savage:

> Many have . . . wasted oil and labour, because, not being practical in the research of objects in nature, being acquainted only with books, being led astray by certain erroneous physical systems, and having made no magnetical experiments, they constructed certain ratiocinations on a basis of mere opinions, and old-womanisly dreamt the things that were not . . . Many others I pass by of purpose . . . who . . . like furbishers send forth ancient things dressed with new names and tricked in an apparel of new words as in prostitutes' finery; . . . who seem to transmit from hand-to-hand, as it were, erroneous teachings in every science and out of their own store now and again to add somewhat of error.[3]

Gilbert practised what he preached. The spirit in which he set up and described his experiments is absolutely modern. He allowed himself, too, some prophetic speculations on gravity — a force which he suggested may be akin to magnetism, pulling stones towards the ground and having to do with the motion of the planets . . .

But the centre of the scientific stage still belonged, rightfully, to the separate disciplines of astronomy and mechanics. After millennia of gazing at the stars and planets, of wondering about their motion, these two disciplines were about to unite to give birth to modern science. From Copernicus to Newton, the process would take less than two hundred years.

At the close of the Middle Ages *Nicholas, Bishop of Cusa* (1401-64) believed already in an infinite universe and in a rotating Earth. With remarkable acumen, he showed himself willing to join astronomy with physics, ascribing the persistence of the Earth's rotation to an original impetus, or momentum, imparted at the time of its creation. He understood, too, the concept of relative motion — the reason why we have no direct sensory clues to the Earth's rotation.

It was then, also, that Johann Mueller of Konigsberg, alias *Regiomontanus* (1436-76), built the first European observatory. Child prodigy, true genius and author of a treatise on trigonometry, he planned a total reform of astronomy but died at the age of forty. He complained vociferously of the misuses of intellectual authority by his contemporaries (1464):

> . . . I cannot get over my amazement at the mental inertia of our astronomers in general who, like credulous women, believe what they read in the books, tablets, and commentaries as if it were the divine and unalterable truth; they believe the authors and neglect the truth.[4]

In one of his last letters, he wrote:

> It is necessary to alter the motion of the stars a little because of the motion of the earth

— which some scholars interpret as referring to the annual revolution around the sun.[4] At the time of Regiomontanus' death, Copernicus — the consecrated hero of the heliocentric model — was three years old.

Nicolas Copernicus (Koppernigk) was born in 1473 in Torun, on the Vistula, son of a prosperous wholesale copper dealer. He was ten when his father died and he became the charge of his uncle Lucas Wazelrode, soon to be Bishop of Ermland, a personage of strong character who took good care of his nieces and nephews. Nicolas, uncle Lucas' favourite, was a quiet and self-effacing young man. He attended the University of Cracow, then went to Bologna and Padua — a total of fourteen years (1491-1506) studying philosophy, law, mathematics, medicine, astronomy and Greek. While his academic record appears to have been unremarkable, he was assiduous enough and emerged with a degree of Doctor of Law. In the meantime (1497) his uncle had secured for him the post of Canon of Frauenberg Cathedral — ensuring Copernicus a comfortable, undemanding, life-long prebend. The young man's studies and, later, his employment as uncle Lucas' personal secretary and physician, earned him a leave of fifteen years. Only in 1512 did he return to Silesia, following his uncle's sudden death (the bishop, it was rumoured, died poisoned by the Teutonic Knights whose influence he helped curtail).

And so Copernicus joined the other fifteen canons of the Cathedral in a comfortable, uneventful existence within the fortified walls of Frauenberg. His town residence was a tower of the wall, overlooking the shallow inland waters of the Frisches Hoff, with its west winds and chill autumn fogs. The bleak northern winters and harsh Baltic storms must have been hard on the good canon who had spent much of his life in sunnier climes and who at forty was, by the standards of his time, an elderly man. Yet here, in his tower, he spent his later years — almost half of his life — a drab, aging cleric, devoting himself methodically to the administration of Church estates in Alenstein, Muhlsack and Ermland. The time of the Reformation and the Renaissance was a glittering era; like most periods of turmoil it was full of dramatic characters — the Borgias, Luther, Machiavelli, Rabelais, Michelangelo, Paracelsus. It is odd to contemplate against this background the quiet, colourless figure of Copernicus and to reflect that this timid man, who all his life strove hard to remain invisible, did more to help change our view of the universe than any of his scintillating contemporaries. There is no record of his having displayed much brilliance during his long and uneventful career at Frauenberg. In his lifetime he only published two books. The first was a 1509 translation from the Greek of a collection of epistles by an obscure Byzantine historian, Theophylactos Simocatta. What possessed Copernicus to translate this little book is problematical (Koestler describes it as inane, pompous and boring). Had this been his only publication, he would have rested for all time in the undistinguished obscurity for which he seemed destined. But by 1512 he had composed a set of notes, which he circulated in manuscript form, under the title of 'A brief outline (Commentariolus) of Nicolas Copernicus' hypotheses on the heavenly motions' — the *Commentariolus*, for short.

The concept he offered — that of an Earth and planets moving around a central sun — seemed, early in the sixteenth century, strangely bold. It accounted for the daily revolution of the firmament and the rise and setting of the sun by assuming that the Earth spun on its axis. And to explain the absence of detectable parallax motion of the stars, Copernicus inferred these to be much further from us than the sun — i.e., he postulated a universe far bigger than had been thought. The idea was not original; Philolaos had proposed something like it 2,000 years before and Aristarchos has suggested a heliocentric model 1,800 years earlier — he too had assumed that the Earth spun on its axis and had concluded that the absence of measurable yearly parallax implied enormous distances (from a heavily scored out passage in a later manuscript, it seems that Copernicus was acquainted with Aristarchos' model). Nevertheless, Copernicus' contribution is to have introduced and consolidated the heliocentric system in Western thought. It was an important *milestone*, rather than, as often claimed, a genuine scientific revolution. The system was conceptually simpler, and thus aesthetically more pleasing than Ptolemy's — although this too is debatable. Thus, according to I.B. Cohen,[5]

> . . . the claim for a greater simplicity of the Copernican system, as opposed to a great complexity of the Ptolemaic system must . . . — insofar as the number of circles is concerned — be taken *cum grano salis*, in fact with the whole saltcellar

Copernicus, a good Aristotelian, was stuck fast on the idea of steady circular motions. Indeed *he* saw the principal merit of his model in the reinstauration of uniform circular motions as the central axiom of astronomy. So he used epicycles and deferents to explain the detail of planetary wanderings across the sky. There have been arguments about the actual number of circles required in the Copernican model. The thirty-four claimed in the Commentariolus may have been later increased to forty-eight — not far different from the number used in updated Ptolemaic versions. The Copernican model was *not* more accurate than Ptolemy's — both led to errors of a couple of degrees in predicting planetary positions. And it was not based on observations: in his whole lifetime, in his thirty lonely years in Frauemberg, Copernicus made only a few dozen observations.

As for Aristarchos' model, our information is scanty and second-hand. Conceivably, it could have been unencumbered by epicycles and deferents — and may thus, for all we know, have been more modern in spirit than its Copernican offspring. Someday, perhaps, a newly discovered manuscript will give us the answer; but it seems unlikely.

Copernicus and his followers used his model, rather than Ptolemy's, for calendrical work — even though it is questionable whether this really simplified the calculations. The Roman Church sought Copernicus' advice on revisions of the calendar and actively encouraged him to publish. During his life it saw him neither as a heretic nor as a threat to its authority.

Copernicus, indeed, was no revolutionary. He was an Aristotelian, a conservative who clung to traditional modes of thought, apprehensive of the changes threatening his world. His correspondence suggests a pusillanimous character, astonishingly willing to efface himself before authority, even by medieval standards. For instance, after receiving in 1541 a letter and epigram for his forthcoming book from Johannes Dantiscus, then Bishop of Ermland and Copernicus' superior in the Church:

> I have received Your Most Revd Lordship's most humane and entirely intimate letter, in which he has condescended to send

> me an epigram addressed to the readers of my book, soberly
> elegant and suited, not to my deserts, but to the extraordinary
> benevolence with which Your Revd Lordship is wont to honour
> scholars . . . Indeed, I desire sofar as I have the power to earn
> it, to gratify the extraordinary benevolence and paternal affec-
> tion towards me whereby Your Revd Lordship does not cease
> to honour me . . .[4]

He was an able mathematician, an erudite scholar and astronomer, a systematic and conscientious synthesiser. But his ideas
were not original. One cannot help thinking that intellectually
Copernicus did not have the brilliance of, say, Leonardo; yet
his influence on science has been far greater. In the history
of ideas, he was simply the right man in the right place at the
right time — someone who, even while doing his life's work,
was unaware of the celebrity it would earn him after his death.
In the 1530s Copernicus wrote up a detailed description of his
model. But timorous as ever, and, above all, fearing ridicule,
he slipped his *magnum opus* in a drawer and abandoned it. And
there it would have stayed had it not been for *Georg Rheticus*
— an interesting character who appeared on the Copernican
horizon in the last years of the great man's life.

Georg Joachim von Laufen was born in 1514 in the Austrian
Tyrol, in what had been ancient Rhoetia, and latinised his name
accordingly. A gifted and mercurial young man, he became
professor of mathematics at the university of Wittenberg at
the age of twenty-two. An early convert to the sun-centred
cosmology of the *Commentariolus*, a protégé of Melanchton, the
influential Lutheran theologian, he took leave in 1539 to visit
canon Copernicus in Ermland. He arrived at the time of the
great anti-Lutheran purge, but as a visiting scholar remained
unharmed.

It was through Rheticus' talents of suasion that Copernicus'
book was published, albeit with a great deal of foot-dragging
by the old canon. The development of events was unusual
— perhaps unique in the annals of science. Boldness not
being Copernicus' strong point, it was agreed that the first
to stick his neck out in print — to, so to speak, test the
waters — should be young Rheticus, who would affix his
name to a kind of preliminary prospectus (which, however,
would credit Copernicus with the ideas therein). This was

to be entitled the First Account or *Narratio Prima*. It speaks much for Rheticus' quicksilver talents that he completed this on 23rd September 1539, a mere ten weeks after his arrival on the scene. The pamphlet — the first *printed* account of the Copernican system, came out in Danzig in February 1540. It was quickly snapped up and another edition appeared in Basel. As Rheticus had foreseen, the pressure on Copernicus to publish a full description of the theory began to mount. By summer, thanks again to Rheticus' coaxings, he gave in. Rheticus then spent a year (until September 1541) copying by hand and checking the entire 424-page manuscript. Printing began in Nuremberg in May 1542.

Rheticus left Nuremberg before the job was finished. There is more than a hint, in a contemporary letter by Melanchton, that he *had to* leave because of trouble — possibly due to his homosexuality. He arranged to leave the supervision of the printing in the hands of Andreas Osiander — a respected theologian, one of the cofounders of Lutheranism and, unlike Luther and Melanchton, an enthusiast of the Copernican theory. But Osiander appended a preface which contained the following admonitions:

> For these hypotheses need not be true or even probable; if they provide a calculus consistent with the observations, that alone is sufficient . . . So far as hypotheses are concerned, let no one expect anything certain from astronomy, which cannot furnish it, lest he accept as the truth ideas conceived for another purpose, and depart from his study a greater fool than when he entered it, Farewell.

Copernicus read this shortly before his death and was much distressed. Yet there seems little doubt that Osiander, who believed himself to be mirroring Copernicus' own caution, acted in good faith; a philosopher in his own right, he was merely expressing legitimate ('instrumentalist') reservations. The moral, perhaps, is that one should not entrust one's manuscript to a philosopher.*

* With apologies to my friend Mark Headlee, who *is* a philosopher and read portions of my manuscript. His helpful and perceptive comments have had, as far as I can tell, no ill effects upon either of us.

To Osiander's cautious disclaimer is added Copernicus' own preface, addressed to Pope Paul III:

> Thinking therefore within myself that to ascribe movement to the Earth must indeed seem an absurd performance on my part to those who know that many centuries have consented to the establishment of the contrary judgment . . . I hesitated long whether . . . it were better to follow the example of the Pythagoreans and others who were wont to impart their philosophical mysteries only to intimates and friends, and then not in writing but by word of mouth . . . In my judgment they did so not, as some would have it, through jealousy in sharing their doctrines, but fearing lest these so noble and hardly won discoveries of the learned should be despised by such as either care not to study save for gain, or — if by the encouragement and example of others they are stimulated to philosophic liberal pursuits — yet by reason of the dullness of their wits are in the company of philosophers as drones among bees. Reflecting thus, the thought of the scorn which I had to fear on account of my novelty and incongruity of my theory, well-nigh induced me to abandon my project.

For a book which was to have such powerful repercussions, this exudes a strangely tentative spirit.

There is also a shameful aspect to the story. In explaining how he overcame his reluctance to publish, Copernicus adds:

> These misgivings and actual protests have been overcome by my friends. First among these was Nicholaus Schonberg, Cardinal of Capua, a man renowned in every department of learning. Next was one who loved me well, Tiedemann Giese, Bishop of Kulm, a devoted student of sacred and all other good literature, who often urged and even importuned me to publish this work which I had kept in store not for nine years only, but for a fourth period of nine years. The same request was made to me by many other eminent and learned men.

The name of Rheticus, the guiding spirit, inspirer and organizer of the publication, is nowhere mentioned. There can be little doubt that this omission was deliberate. Rheticus' reputation in the Catholic hierarchy was poor on several counts. He was a Lutheran and, probably, a homosexual; so Copernicus betrays him.

In December 1542 Copernicus suffered a stroke; he died on 24th May 1543. His friend Bishop Giese wrote of his last days to Rheticus:

> For many days he had been deprived of his memory and mental vigour; he only saw his completed book at the last moment, on the day he died.

Rheticus himself, after a peripatetic and not very successful career as mathematician and astronomer died in Hungary in 1576 — an unsung scientific hero of the Reformation.

De Revolutionibus Orbis Coelestium is one of the strangest books in the history of science. It is generally conceded to be a milestone — an appreciation one need not quarrel with; progress, after all, is a relative notion and milestones are, to some extent, a matter of convention. Yet in this work, Copernicus seems to have offered the world his heliocentric model on totally inadequate grounds. His motivation appears to have been largely irrational — an intuition, perhaps, combined with the conviction that such a system was simpler and more pleasing than Ptolemy's. Such points are, of course, infinitely debatable.

To Copernicus' credit, and despite Osiander's disclaimers, he believed explicitly in the reality of the Earth's motion. Herein may lie his one true claim to greatness. But he never resolved one of the principal problems confronting the theory in his day: how to reconcile the fact that a stone falls vertically on a rapidly moving Earth. To the medieval mind, and to most of Copernicus' contemporaries, it seemed self-evident that the stone would tend to be left behind and fall sidewise, i.e., west of its point of release on a spinning Earth. Since no such effect was observed, it was reasonable to assume that the Earth was at rest. In dealing with this point, Copernicus' arguments were feeble and Aristotelian:

> . . . heavy falling objects, being specially earthy, must doubtless retain the nature of the whole to which they belong.'
>
> 'Further, we conceive immobility to be nobler and more divine than change and inconstancy, which latter is thus more appropriate to Earth than to the universe. Would it not then seem absurd to ascribe motion to that which contains or

locates, and not rather to that contained and located, namely the Earth?

His fixation on steady circular motion and epicycles was likewise a clinging to the past. While he understood full well the uses of mathematics to support his model, the imperatives of Aristotelian perfection were as important to him as *saving the phenomena* — or, to put it in modern language, as having the theory agree with observation. Copernicus, in other words, offers us a strange paradox: a conservative, medieval mind, living in an era of extraordinary ferment, desperately afraid of change, yet producing — reluctantly — a work whose *impact* was to be far-reaching and revolutionary.

De Revolutionibus is well-nigh unreadable. A conscientious if unoriginal mathematician, Copernicus argues his case with calculations, drawings and endless circumlocution. The hard core of the book, its heliocentric message, is far from new: it merely revives 1800 year-old, or even more ancient, ideas. Hobbled as it is with *a priori* Aristotelianisms — such as the necessity of circular motions — it offers little of methodological interest. The model fails to save the phenomena any better than Ptolemy's. But the concept is simpler, and Copernicus believed that his motions were a model of reality — a point weakened by Osiander's unsolicited introduction. Only a small number of people in the sixteenth century understood the significance of his work; the first edition of a thousand copies was never sold out. Its importance is historical. It was the final break with the comfortable, small, enclosed medieval cosmos — a deliberate step along a line of thought which would reveal a universe hostile to life, vast and lonely beyond expectation. It was also subversive, contradicting cherished biblical phrases (*and Joshua commanded the sun to stand still*); *and* it removed mankind from the centre of creation. Yet the Church of Rome appears not to have responded to the printing of *De Revolutionibus*; it had actually encouraged Copernicus to publish — perhaps, in this respect, Osiander's preface had served a good purpose. The Lutherans, however, reacted strongly. Melanchton is reported to have said that, in the face of such theorizing, 'wise men should tame the unrestraint of men's minds'. Calvin, appealing to the words of the psalm *The world also is established, that it cannot be moved*, said: 'Who will venture to place the authority of Copernicus above that of the Holy Spirit?' After the appearance of the Commentariolus, already, Luther had responded with: 'This fool wants to turn the whole of astronomy upside down.' Perhaps Copernicus was no genius; but fool he was not.

After Copernicus, the next step towards a modern view of the heavens was taken by *Tycho de Brahe* (1546-1601), who vastly improved the accuracy of astronomical observations. A carousing, Rabelaisian Danish nobleman with a silver nose-bridge (he lost the original in a youthful duel), he was the antithesis of Copernicus — colourful, self-assertive and an enthusiastic observer of the heavens. He was the first great experimental astronomer of the modern age, and obtained the most accurate astronomical data of the pre-telescopic era. He did this through the use of bigger, more carefully constructed instruments giving accuracies of the order of minutes of arc. He also realized the value of continuous sequences of observations for defining orbits.

Tycho quite rightly became convinced that neither the Ptolemaic nor the Copernican models conformed to observation. He therefore proposed his own system — a kind of compromise between the ancient ones of Herakleides of Pontos and Aristarchos — in which all planets other than the Earth orbited the sun, and the sun circled the Earth. Unable to resolve the puzzle of the vertically falling stone and unlike Copernicus, unwilling to fudge the issue, he drew what seemed to be the only honest conclusion: the Earth was stationary!

Tycho earned much fame by observing a brilliant new star, the supernova of 1572 — in obvious and flagrant contradiction to still prevalent Aristotelian edicts concerning the perfection and immutability of the heavens. But his greatest contribution to science were his painstaking measurements of planetary motions, the quality of which reached the limits of what could be achieved by non-telescopic methods. No one before had accumulated such a treasure-trove of detailed and reliable information. Far more accurate than Ptolemy's, or even Regiomontanus' best, his data held the key to the true motion of the planets.

Tycho de Brahe was born to all the economic and social advantages of the high aristocracy, and Copernicus enjoyed the protection and patronage of influential relatives. But *Johannes Kepler* (1571-1630) suffered from most of the disadvantages of a lowly birth in the sixteenth century: overcrowding, poor health, narrow family horizons. The odds against him were phenomenal. His father was a rogue who had to flee the gallows, his great-aunt was burnt as a witch; had it not been for Kepler's devotion in later years, his mother would have suffered the same fate. As a child Johannes suffered from an infinite variety of ailments, eczemas, intestinal diseases; at the age of four he almost died of smallpox. He attended school irregularly until the age of thirteen, when he was taken into the Lutheran theological seminary of Adelberg. His one stroke of luck in life was to be born in Wurtemberg where a bright boy could get a free education. And Kepler was a brilliant student. He went on to the University of Tuebingen where his astronomy and mathematics teacher, Maestlin, instilled him with faith in the Copernican system. In 1593 he was appointed to teach at the Protestant school in Gratz. He appears to have been a poor teacher, making frequent errors, getting involved in asides, and losing his students. It is reported that in his first year he had only a few students, and in his second none at all. It was during a lecture that Kepler glimpsed the idea which was to inspire his whole professional life (9th July 1595 — he kept careful autobiographical notes). This was an extraordinary, wrongheaded, wild, Platonic vision of the intrinsic importance of the five regular polyhedra in the ordering of the cosmos. He justified his position in religious terms:

> Why waste words? Geometry existed before the Creation, is co-eternal with the mind of God, is God himself (what exists in God that is not God himself?); geometry provided God with a model for the Creation and was implanted into man, together with God's own likeness — and not merely conveyed to his mind through the eyes.[4]

It had to be possible, thought Kepler, to *deduce* the structure of the universe from *a priori* axioms. What could be more plausible than to assume that, in a Copernican universe, the distribution of the spheres holding the planetary orbits should be regulated by some beautiful symmetry principle? And what could be more natural than a system of nested regular polyhedra! In his *Mysterium Cosmographicum*, written at the age of twenty-five, Kepler explains how to construct such a system. With characteristic eagerness, he sent a copy of his work to Galileo, whose reputation was already growing. Galileo acknowledged it with polite, if restrained enthusiasm.

The model of the *Mysterium* represented the medieval dimension in Kepler's thinking, which still assumed it possible to deduce the structure of the universe from purely rational, *a priori* considerations untempered by observational data. He was to spend uncounted years trying to fit good astronomical data to this aberrant vision. But Kepler's thought was *also* in part modern — for he believed in comparing his models carefully with observation. And, being a man of great integrity and thoroughness, he would eventually concede that the data did not fit. Yet, strange as this model may look to us, it would not have seemed so to his contemporaries. And it was to lead him, by dint of much labour, slowly and serendipitously, to the discoveries upon which rests his everlasting fame.

By the end of the sixteenth century young Archduke Ferdinand of Hapsburg, the great counter-reformer, had already embarked upon his life-long avocation of hounding Protestants. In 1599 Kepler's school was closed. Kepler himself was not affected: as an already famous scholar he had well-wishers in both camps. His Catholic friends, indeed, hoped to convert him. But to von Hohenburg, the Catholic Chancellor of Bavaria, he wrote:

> I am a Christian, the Lutheran creed was taught me by my parents, I took it unto myself with repeated searchings of its foundations, with daily questionings, and I hold fast to it. Hypocrisy I have never learnt. I am earnest about my faith and I do not play with it.[4]

By closing the school in Graz, Ferdinand unwittingly rendered his major service to history: Kepler was forced to look for new pastures. On 1st January 1600 he decided to leave for Prague to visit Tycho de Brahe — an easily remembered date and one most fateful for science.

Kepler's association with Tycho was brief and stormy. He knew that the famous Dane had the most accurate astronomical data in history. He knew, too, that what Tycho wanted from him was unequivocal support for the Tychonian model of the solar system — in which he, Kepler, did not believe. In the Copernican and Ptolemaic systems the biggest discrepancies between theory and observation occurred for Mars, the wandering red planet whose departures from its assigned orbits were a kind of permanent astronomical scandal. It was to the study of Mars that Tycho assigned his new collaborator — hoping no doubt for some miraculous resolution of this problem which, of course, also bedevilled his own system. The twenty-two months during which Kepler collaborated with Tycho were immensely frustrating for him. He soon realized that his chances of getting a free hand with the Dane's data were slim. Several times the great men quarrelled, only to make up again — each needed the other, and both knew it. What began to look like a hopeless problem in human relations was resolved with undignified finality when, in October 1601, following an unusually prolonged and magnificent banquet during which Tycho grossly overindulged, failed to relieve himself in good time, and died.[4] His last words, referring no doubt to his Tychonian system, are reputed to have been: 'let me not seem to have lived in vain.' He need not have worried; his life's work proved priceless — if not quite in the way he had hoped for.

Two important events stemmed from Tycho's death. First, Kepler inherited his job as Imperial Mathematicus to the Emperor Rudolph II; his future was now secure for as long as Rudolph lived. Second, he appropriated Tycho's measurements — before numerous quarrelsome and ignorant relatives could do so. Thus, by a series of historical accidents it came about that Europe's most able, industrious and intellectually honest mathematician came into possession of what were then the most accurate astronomical observations in history.

The ensuing years were critical. Now in his thirties, at the height of his intellectual powers, Kepler focussed on Tycho's data — searching for those simple symmetries his mind had conceived when he had been a teacher in Graz. It is an attestation to Kepler's integrity and essential modernity that, while concluding that the observations would not bend to his desires, he discovered the first two of the famous laws that bear his name. Numbered in sequence reverse to the order of their discovery, these are:

1. A planet's orbit is an ellipse, with the sun at one focus.
2. The line from planet to sun sweeps out equal areas in equal times.

These were first published in his *Astronomia Nova* (1609). Unlike Galileo, Newton, Maxwell, Einstein — unlike almost all major or minor scientists to have published their research — Kepler documents every step on the road to his discoveries. He offers us a candid record of one of history's most eminent scientific minds at work, discovering the laws which would allow Newton to establish his theory of universal gravitation and thus provide the foundations for the development of European physics. Kepler shows us, step by step, how he was forced to revise his ideas. He had to throw away the crippling preconceptions of all previous models — such as the 'perfection' and sacrosanctity of circular motion. What appears to have given him the courage to do so was his remarkable conviction that the solar system was governed by forces emanating from the sun. He in fact introduced physics into astronomy, in the form of two competing forces — one sun-centred, the other belonging to the planet. And while his forces were off the mark, this was a vital step in the right direction.

In documenting his feats, Kepler displays a disarming honesty. He gives us all the errors, false turns, corrections. It is a wondrous tale, an incredible saga of blind alleys, cancelling arithmetical errors, false reasonings — an example of what Koestler so aptly described as a kind of creative sleepwalking. As he finally alights upon his first law, Kepler exclaims:

Ah what a foolish bird I have been!

Nine years later, Kepler discovered his *third law*. It states:

> 3. The squares of the periods of revolution of the planets are to one another as the cubes of the major axes of their orbits.

This result appeared in print in 1618, in Kepler's last big work: Harmony of the World — *Harmonice Mundi*. Finished a few months after the death of his daughter Katherine, a few days after the sack of Prague and during the years in which his mother was being persecuted for witchcraft, there appears to have been no intentional irony in the title. The harmonies Kepler had in mind did not belong to this world — nor to any we know of. Here was the culmination of years of effort to put the universe into a symmetric, neo-Platonic or Pythagorean frame. And once again, incredibly, out of a morass of numerology and preconception, one sees emerge a valid law — one of the cornerstones of modern science. In his preface, Kepler exults:

> Having perceived the first glimmer of dawn eighteen months ago, the light of day three months ago, but only a few days ago the plain sun of a most wonderful vision — nothing shall now hold me back. Yes, I give myself up to holy raving. I mockingly defy all mortals with this open confession: I have   robbed the golden vessels of the Egyptians to make out of them a tabernacle for my God, far from the frontiers of Egypt. If you forgive me, I shall rejoice. If you are angry, I shall bear it. Behold, I have cast the dice, and I am writing a book either for my contemporaries, or for posterity. It is all the same to me. It may wait a hundred years for a reader, since God has also waited six thousand years for a witness . . .[4]

Seventy years later, give or take a few, Newton would be his witness — re-deriving Kepler's laws mathematically, from first principles.

Towards the end of his life Kepler published astronomical tables based on de Brahe's work: the *Rudolphine tables*, which remained essential for astronomers and navigators well into the eighteenth century. His contributions to science were not limited to astronomy. In the period preceding his discovery of the third law, stimulated by the invention of the telescope and the wonders revealed thereby by Galileo, he founded the new discipline of geometrical optics. He admired Galileo and tried to establish contact with him several times, without much success. There is little doubt that the fault was Galileo's; however, what led Galileo to ignore his brilliant colleague from the north is unclear. He wrote to Kepler twice — once to thank him for a book, and once to ask for his support.

Kepler died on 15th November 1630. The cemetery in which he was buried was destroyed in the Thirty Years War.

In tracing the emergence of modern science, it is probably right to see the developments in astronomy, mathematics and physics as crucial. It is the fusion of these, accomplished by the likes of Kepler, Galileo and later, Newton, that forged the powerful and subtle interplay of theory and experiment that *is* modern science — the paradigm, the model to which all branches of human knowledge would aspire. Copernicus prodded our consciousness in the direction of a sun-centred solar system. Kepler found the laws of motion of the planets. Newton *explained* these in terms of mathematical hypotheses or theories, having a secure experimental or empirical basis. Before this could be accomplished, it took a new breed of thinker — men like Tycho de Brahe, Kepler, Gilbert, Galileo — to free natural philosophy of the scholasticism of the Middle Ages. A spur to this was the growth of the utilitarian aspect of science — an outlook which said, in effect, that knowledge is power and which was to render the whole endeavour palatable and interesting to society. Its spokesman and propagandist was *Francis Bacon* (1561-1626). Philosopher rather than scientist, his role in the history of science, nevertheless, has been substantial. More than anyone he gave the world its rationale for supporting such activities. Possessed of a lucid and elegant literary style he was, in truth, the prophet to our modern technocracy. As Thomas Sprat put it, in his 1667 *History of the Royal Society*, Bacon was 'One great man, who had the true Imagination of the whole state of the Enterprise.'

Bacon was born in London in 1561. His father, Sir Nicholas Bacon, was Keeper of the Great Seal. At the age of twelve Francis went to Trinity College, Cambridge, and at sixteen he joined the staff of the English ambassador to France. His father died unexpectedly in 1579, leaving him without an estate. So Bacon had to climb the ladder to prominence and power by his own efforts and wit — of which he had a great deal. He was lucky, or shrewd, in his choice of friends. The handsome young Earl of Essex, Elizabeth's favourite, became his patron and protector; in fact, he made Bacon the gift of an estate in Twickenham. This did not keep Bacon from taking part in Essex's eventual prosecution — a role which earned him many enemies. But none could arrest his upward progress. In 1613, he became Attorney General; in 1618, Lord Chancellor. His downfall came in 1621 when he was accused of bribery. He spent the last five years of his life in solitude, disgraced, but busy with philosophy and writing.

He had planned a major opus: *The Great Instauration*, the purpose of which was to establish a method for obtaining reliable new knowledge in *all* its forms. It would, said Bacon, effectively restore man's dominion over nature, lost in the fall from Paradise. The task was over-ambitious and, not surprisingly, was never finished. In his first volume, *The Advancement of Learning*, Bacon pointed out the sterility of scholasticism and emphasised the superiority of the empirical method of gaining knowledge. As illustration he offered the explosion of knowledge created by travel in the fifteenth and sixteenth centuries: *Multi pertransibut et augebitur scientia* (many travel and the sciences flourish), read the frontispiece.

Bacon's principal work of scientific philosophy was the *Novum Organum*. He gave therein a critique of reasoning, a kind of *negative* epistemology, in which he identified the principal errors (idols) committed by traditional philosophies. At the same time he proposed a *positive* epistemology — his method of *induction*. He saw this as the extraction of laws out of an orderly arrangement of data. This is a simple enough process; yet its logical foundations are suspect. One thing we *have* understood since Bacon's time, is that, in using induction, the framing of preliminary hypotheses is essential. Since Bacon omits this, his method was, in practice, unworkable.

Bacon is famous for his espousal of scientific knowledge as a source of power:

For there is no strength that can break the causal chain: Nature
cannot be conquered but by obeying her. Accordingly these
twin goals, human science and human power, come in the end
to be one. To be ignorant of causes is to be frustrated in action.

His understanding of the pitfalls of such power is entirely
modern — even more pertinent to us, perhaps, than to his
contemporaries:

Yet out of the same fountain come instruments of lust, and
also instruments of death. For (not to speak of the arts of the
procurers) the most exquisite poisons, as well as guns, and
such-like engines of destruction, are the fruits of mechanical
invention; and well we know how far in cruelty and destructive-
ness they exceeded the Minotaur himself.

'Lastly, I would address one general admonition to all; that they
consider what are the true ends of knowledge, and that they
seek it not either for pleasure of mind, or for contention, or for
profit, or fame, or power, or any of these inferior things; but for
the benefit and use of life; and that they perfect and govern it
in charity. For it was for lust of power that the angels fell, from
the lust of knowledge that men fell; but of charity there can be
no excess, neither did angel or man ever come to danger by it.

Amen.

Bacon's *New Atlantis*, a short work of fantasy, offers us a
scientific Utopia, a society in which, as H.G. Wells would
put it: 'At last science has its proper place as the master of
things.' An ideal of the sort that has haunted many a thinker, a
kind of model anarchy governed by knowledge and wisdom, it
embodies a romantic view of science and power. More recent
utopias have hardly progressed beyond it; the technical fancies
of H.G. Wells or B.F. Skinner may be more up to date, but the
basic naiveté is still there — presupposing of human nature that
for which there is little historical evidence. In this work Bacon
comes across as an idealist who believes that sense and good
will in people must lead to a perfect society. And this is odd for
in his own life he seems to have been hard-nosed and cynical
— the embodiment of Machiavelli's new man. He was fond of
a quote from one of the seven wise men of ancient Greece,
Bias of Priene, who counselled all to 'love your friend as if he

were to become your enemy, and your enemy as if he were to become your friend.' In his essay *Of Wisdom for a Man's Self* he says: 'Wisdom for a man's self is the wisdom of rats, that will be sure to leave a house somewhat before it falls'. He seems to have succeeded rather well in putting these admonitions into practice; his part in the prosecution, leading to the execution, of his unstinting protector the Earl of Essex was questionable — some say sinister.

Bacon died in the pursuit of empirical knowledge — from a chill contracted while gathering snow to demonstrate that a fowl would not rot if kept at low temperature. 'He is thus,' says Bertrand Russell, 'a rarity among philosophers in that he was killed by his own ideas.'[6]

Taking us from the particular to the general, induction is a process that has always made philosophers uncomfortable. It is a distinct and essential stage in the acquiring and ordering of experience; but, as Hume pointed out, it cannot lead to certainty, i.e., to *necessary* truths. Whewell, the nineteenth-century Cambridge science philosopher, said that induction and deduction went, respectively, up and down the same staircase. Whilst Bacon was, in this way, instructing natural philosophers to go *upstairs*, his great French contemporary *René Descartes* was telling them to go *down*. One of history's great apologists of the deductive process, Descartes (1596-1650) deduced a whole cosmology from *a priori* principles. A dualist, he drew a sharp distinction between the worlds of thought and matter. In the former he was a highly original and independent thinker, with his *Method of Doubt* and his famous *Cogito* establishing the one incontrovertible fact from which he starts — the fact of his own existence. Many consider him the father of modern European philosophy. But deduction is only as good as the premises on which it stands and, in dealing with the world of matter, Descartes came to some odd conclusions. He began by accepting the basic Aristotelian premise of the universe as a packed plenum with no space left unfilled. From this it followed, via some tortuous logic, that the universe should be seen as a collection of eddies or vortices in a kind of universal aether — which, according to Descartes, explained both gravity and the motion of the planets. But this object lesson in the dangers of pure deduction is not what science remembers Descartes for. His seminal contributions were in physics and mathematics. He was the first to state explicitly and accurately the principle that a body subject to no force must be either at rest or in a state of uniform motion. This was the modern principle of inertia, coming more than a thousand years after John Philoponus formulated the idea of impetus.

Descartes also created a new branch of mathematics — analytical geometry — which would allow much of modern mechanics and science to be formulated in mathematical terms. Basic here was the introduction of *coordinates* — without which neither physicists nor stockbrokers could function properly. Cartesian cosmology may have had little to recommend it, but Cartesian mathematics was a huge step forward.

Cartesian deduction and Baconian induction are, in some ways, complementary. Neither by itself offers a royal road to knowledge. When fused they appear to offer something resembling a method. Many modern scientists are likely to see themselves as compromising between them — using a combination of hypotheses based on induction (from experiment) and mathematics (deduction). This is sometimes referred to as the hypothetico-deductive model of science. Yet today, still, more than three centuries after Bacon and Descartes, harmony does not reign among philosophers of science. Many in fact deny the existence of *any* method — a position not without merit, when one recalls the mental acrobatics of a Copernicus or a Kepler.

CHAPTER NINE

Galileo

'Fame,' said Francis Bacon, 'is like a river that beareth up things light and swollen and drowning things weighty and solid.' This is an apposite aphorism for the figure of Galileo Galilei (1564-1642). His image as a defender of truth, victim of the Inquisition, martyr of science who escaped the flames by a whisker and a recantation, all that for which he is best known to the public is, for the historian of ideas, the light and swollen aspect of his reputation. That famous quarrel was a battle of ideologies, a struggle for power over men's minds in which Galileo was a reluctant, almost unwitting actor; no scientific issue rested on its outcome. The Copernican system, which Galileo defended, was already ascendant. Indeed, at the time of his trial, it was out of date, having been superseded by Kepler's model — which Galileo, for reasons best known to himself, chose to ignore. Modern accounts of Galileo's quarrel with the Church of Rome suggest that it was unnecessary; but it *is* historically interesting, if only for the light it sheds on the man and upon the attitudes of the seventeenth-century Roman Church.

For the scientist the weighty and solid parts of Galileo's reputation lie elsewhere — in his insights into experimental physics, in his use of mathematics for the solution of concrete problems and particularly in his work on motion and mechanics — the basic theorems of which, laid down by him, are cornerstones of Western physics and modern science. In this, and in the wrenching of science away from metaphysics, lies Galileo's real importance. He was the first modern *scientist*.

Born in Florence, in the same year as Shakespeare, his father was an outstanding musicologist, a cultured man of modest means and radical leanings. Despite being a brilliant student, young Galileo failed to get a scholarship at the University of

Pisa and left before completing his studies; yet he had already discovered that a pendulum swings with a period independent of its amplitude (providing this is moderate) — a discovery which, in other hands, would lead to a new mechanism in clocks. He began his serious studies of mechanics at home, and invented a hydrostatic balance. A description of this, in manuscript form, attracted attention in the academic world and in 1589 secured him a lectureship at the University of Pisa. In 1592 he became professor of mathematics at the more prestigious university of Padua where he remained for eighteen fruitful years. Here, in 1597, he received a copy of Kepler's *Cosmic Mystery*. Galileo acknowledged the gift politely with a letter in which he confided that he too was a believer in the Copernican system. Kepler's reply to Galileo remained unanswered for twelve years.

In Padua Galileo acquired a formidable reputation, powerful patrons and not a few enemies — academics, largely, resentful of his success, brilliance and abrasive wit.

As is true of most great men, Galileo's image is part truth, part myth. Scientists have often seen him as a hero — as the man who invented many of the concepts and attitudes of modern science and suffered martyrdom, or something like it, for defending *the truth*. This is an oversimplification. Galileo certainly *was* the founder of modern mechanics, though the way had been prepared by people like Oresme, Albert of Saxony and Buridan. He *did* contribute profound insights and new instruments through the whole length and breadth of contemporary physics. But his name is surrounded by romantic legend and a tendentious history. Galileo did not invent the telescope, make the first thermometer, or discover the law of inertia; he contributed little to astronomical theory and did not prove the truth of the Copernican system — even if he did defend it. Neither threatened by nor subjected to torture, he never muttered '*eppur si muove*', except in the fevered imagination of an eighteenth century French Abbé. And, as Herbert Butterfield points out, he did not determine the law of free-fall by climbing '. . . the leaning tower of Pisa with a one-hundred pound cannon ball under one arm, and a one-pound cannon ball under the other.'[1]

The Galilean legend rests on two main themes: his battle

with the Church and his founding of modern physics. The two are, of course, connected. Although precisely what led to his trial is still a matter of debate, it is clear that his devastating attacks on Aristotelian orthodoxy earned him many enemies, particularly in the academic world, who either contributed to or outright engineered his downfall.

Galileo's confrontation with the Church of Rome affected the second half of his life. It poisoned his existence and took his attention away from more important things. An enormous amount has been written about this episode, and there are various schools of thought concerning its cause.

The traditional story is that Galileo was a staunch defender of the truth and stood up for Copernicanism because it was true. Persecuted for this by the Church, threatened with torture, he recanted — without the apocryphal rebellious mutterings — was condemned for heresy and imprisoned for the rest of his life. An unsympathetic view is taken by at least one biographer (Koestler) who feels that, on the whole, the Church did its level best to avoid confrontation: Galileo, stung by the attacks of mediocrities, driven by a powerful ego, and ignoring the advice of friends and well-wishers, clashed head on with another egomaniac (Pope Urban VIII), ending up by putting his own neck in the noose.[2] A modern scholar, Stillman Drake, maintains that while Galileo *was* the victim of jealous and mediocre colleagues, his purpose has been misunderstood: this was, actually, to keep the Church from committing a fatal mistake. The issue, in other words, is interesting, complicated, and perhaps far from settled.

Until 1610 Galileo published nothing, preferring to circulate manuscripts, often under pseudonyms, on a variety of topics — some of which involved him in considerable battles. There was, for instance, an argument over the supernova of October 1604 which Galileo, in a series of public lectures, showed to have been located in the heavens — a claim which, like Tycho de Brahe's in 1572, was not acceptable to his colleagues. It was in flagrant opposition to Aristotelian cosmology whose heavenly sphere, consisting of the quintessence, was perfect and immutable. This brought him into sharp conflict with the 'professors of philosophy' like Cesare Cremonini at Padua, who published a pseudonymous pamphlet attacking Galileo. The ideas of ordinary distance used by Galileo, said Cremonini, did not apply to such vast dimensions or to Aristotle's quintessence. To underline his contempt for such arguments, Galileo couched his answer as a dialogue between two peasants — in Paduan dialect. What, says one, do the philosophers know about measuring anything! That was a task for mathematicians — and they do not care whether things are made of quintessence or of polenta.[3]

Another professor, Colombe, published a book on the star and was also attacked by Galileo. Colomba is Italian for dove — and Galileo henceforth dubbed his enemies the *Pigeon League*. There were further quarrels, too, involving priorities of invention and other matters — in all of which Galileo's wit did little to endear him.

A critical date was 1608 — the probable year of the invention of the telescope by Hans Lippershey of Middelburg in Holland. Galileo appears to have learnt of this in 1609, at a time when his finances were poor and he was seeking a rise in salary. Hearing that a Dutchman was on his way to sell a telescope to the Venetians, Galileo quickly put one together and, with the help of a friend, dissuaded the city fathers from buying the foreign device. His was a twenty-power telescope which duly impressed the authorities and secured him some benefits.

Galileo then turned his instrument to the heavens — with remarkable effect. Thus he demonstrated the existence of Jupiter's satellites — which, to flatter the Medicis whose patronage he sought, he named the Medicean stars. This demolished an important argument against the Copernican model which claimed that the Earth could not travel around the sun at great speed without losing its moon: yet Jupiter did so, successfully, with *four* orbiting moons in attendance. He discovered also the mountains of the moon, and showed that the Milky Way consisted of vast numbers of distant, uncharted stars (something Democritos had guessed two thousand years before!). All this appeared in Galileo's first book, which came out in 1610, when he was forty-six years old: *The Starry Messenger* (*Sidereus Nuncius*), dedicated to his erstwhile pupil, Cosimo di Medici. Unlike the learned writings of his colleagues and of most of his predecessors *The Messenger* was terse, to the point, written in the vernacular and immensely readable: its impact was immediate. Faced by the vision of a vastly larger cosmos, the public responded with real excitement; the 'professors of philosophy' reacted with equally genuine hostility. They ridiculed Galileo, accused him of falling prey to optical illusions and, worse yet, of fraud. A Jesuit — Father Clavius — pointed out that there was no proof that anything seen through the glass lenses was real: after all, if you removed the lenses, you saw nothing! Mountains on the moon were anathema to good Aristotelians — who were committed to the view that heavenly bodies had to be *perfect* spheres i.e., perfectly smooth.

As in so many of Galileo's disputes, his opponents depended on philosophical principles; *he* argued from observation and, insofar as he could determine them, from facts. In discussing the Aristotelian idea of the *perfect* sphere, there was, he said, no such thing in Nature as perfection, except perhaps as to use — pointing out, in passing, that spherical bricks were far from perfect for building walls.

Kepler's was one of the few powerful voices raised in Galileo's defence — it seems that he publicly accepted the telescopic observations long before he was able to verify them himself. Galileo was prompted into writing Kepler a further letter — the second and last time he wrote to his amiable northern colleague:

> What is to be done? Let us laugh at the stupidity of the crowd, my Kepler . . . I wish I had more time to laugh with you. How you would shout with laughter, my dearest Kepler, if you were to hear what the chief philosophers of Pisa said against me to the Grand Duke . . . But the night has come and I can no longer converse with you . . .[2]

But of Galileo's recent observations, about which Kepler had inquired, or of Kepler's own great work, there is no mention (It has been suggested that Galileo never accepted the idea of elliptical orbits).

During this period Galileo was also lobbying the Medicis for a permanent post, offering as bait the use of his expertise for

> The practice of fortification, ordinance, assaults, sieges, estimation of distances, artillery matters, the uses of various instruments, and so on.[3]

Galileo's vision of the power of knowledge was crystal clear —

quite modern, in fact. One feels he would have been perfectly at home writing late twentieth-century contract proposals — for, say, the Ministry of Defence. Clearly, he was something of an operator. Thus, when he named the Jovian moons the Medicean Stars, he assured Cosimo di Medici, the Grand Duke of Tuscany, that there were no further stars to be discovered which could be named after someone else. At the same time he wrote to the King of France to tell him that any new stars would be named after *him*.[4]

His efforts paid off several months after the publication of *The Messenger*, when he became philosopher and mathematician to the Grand Duke, and moved to Florence. Here he continued his telescopic observations and first saw the phases of Venus — crescent-like when closest to Earth, round when fully illuminated and on the far side of the sun. This solved a long-standing puzzle concerning variations in the brightness of Venus; it also supported the view that it orbited the sun. Galileo later used this as evidence for the Copernican system — although it could be used equally well to uphold Tycho de Brahe's or Heracleides' models (which Galileo rejected intuitively as dynamically absurd). He also had the clever idea that the motion and eclipses of Jupiter's moons could be used as an accurate celestial clock to determine longitude at sea, making many measurements and compiling tables thereof.

In 1612 Galileo became embroiled in another controversy — this time over the discovery of sunspots, which he had seen in 1611. He had not been the first, however. Thomas Harriot in Oxford had noted their existence before and a Jesuit astronomer, Christopher Scheiner, under the pen-name of Apelles, had written on the very subject. When Galileo published his *Sunspot Letters*, stating he had discovered them, a bitter wrangle ensued. Again the argument evolved along predictable Aristotelian *versus* observational-scientific lines. Scheiner claimed that the sunspots were tiny planets seen against the bright disk of the sun, which *had to* be a perfect and unblemished sphere. Galileo argued that the essence of things is an unknowable irrelevancy — that science must limit itself to observable properties and events, and had nothing at all to say about such things as perfection or the lack of it. But the argument was an angry one and Galileo added another name to a growing list of enemies. It was in the *Sunspot Letters* that Galileo, for the first time, *unequivocally* endorsed in print the Copernican system — in an appendix. He demonstrated here that, to calculate accurately the eclipses of the Jovian moons, one had to make corrections for the *Earth's motion*. He regarded this as the clincher; for, while such corrections could be made on an *ad hoc* basis in the Tychonian or Ptolemaic models, it was only in a heliocentric picture that they acquired a common-sense, physical explanation Galileo was above all else a physical thinker — a *physicist* in the modern sense of the word.

This and related arguments during 1613-16 were important in determining the outcome of Galileo's eventual clash with the Inquisition. By 1613 the issue of Copernicanism had explicitly entered the arena. The professors — The Pigeon League, rather than the theologians — could not accept the motion of the Earth. Their real objections were Aristotelian, but they couched them in theological terms, stating that the rotation of the Earth was contrary to the Scriptures. Galileo responded to such attacks with a series of letters [— one addressed to Father Castelli, a friend of his at the University of Pisa, the other to the Grand Duchess Christina, mother of Cosimo]. Herein he states that, while Nature speaks unambiguously and explicitly for herself, the Bible, — the repository of God's word — uses metaphor. Such arguments, with their whiff of ancient Averroist heresies, suggested a new tactic to Galileo's enemies: in 1615 they tried to drag in the Inquisition. But at this point the Church was not interested in censuring Galileo, and no action was taken; it was not felt that he had strayed into theological territory. As Cardinal Dini, a friendly Church dignitary said to him: 'One might write freely as long as one stays out of the sacristy'. But Galileo's personal foes, and The Pigeon League in particular, kept up their intrigues. In 1615 an unwelcome ally appeared on the scene, in the person of a Carmelite, P.A. Foscarini. He published a book claiming to reconcile Copernicanism and the Bible. A copy was sent to Cardinal Bellarmine (whom Galileo had met some years before, in Padua; one of the men who condemned Giordano Bruno to death at the stake, he was canonised in the twentieth century). Receipt of the book prompted the cardinal to write to Foscarini, telling him that he and Galileo were on theologically sensitive grounds; but as long as they treated the motion of the Earth as a hypothesis rather than fact, no difficulties of a theological nature would arise:[2]

> First, I say it seems to me that your Reverence and Signor Galileo act prudently when you content yourselves with speaking hypothetically and not absolutely, as I have always understood that Copernicus spoke. For to say that the assumption that the Earth moves and the sun stands still saves all the celestial appearances better than do eccentrics and epicycles is to speak with excellent good sense and to run no risk whatever. Such a manner of speaking suffices for a mathematician.

It may have been wise, at this point, for Galileo to accept Bellarmine's suggestion. Galileo's own writings suggest that this would have had little or no substantive effect on his work. The Copernican issue was, to Galileo, merely a side show; it had no relevance to the main body of his scientific work. Yet he chose to ignore the cardinal's advice. The reasons for this are uncertain, and there are various interpretations. The traditional schoolbook view, that it was a matter of principle, a question of truth *versus* obscurantism is too simplistic. More interesting is the thesis of Stillman Drake, a modern Galileo scholar:[5]

> The picture of Galileo's personality presented year by year in his correspondence and publications is that of a prudent man, not given to forming conclusions without having weighed the evidence, well aware of social customs, and disinclined to quarrel with highly placed persons in Church or state.

Galileo, says Drake, was a devout Christian, who felt that it would be a grave mistake for the Church to rule on a scientific question on purely theological grounds. He simply did his best to keep this from happening — with disastrous results for all concerned. Koestler's view is less flattering. He believes that Galileo, a vain and arrogant man, could not stomach continued onslaughts by colleagues whom he knew to be his intellectual inferiors. His involvement became compulsive, and he was unable to pull out in time to side-step the final catastrophe.

Whatever the reason it was then, in 1615, that Galileo took the decision which, eighteen years later, after much wasted time and great anguish, was to lead to his final humiliation at the hands of the Inquisition: he chose to ignore Bellarmine's advice. During the following months he wrote irate letters and lectured in Rome on the Copernican model, pulverizing his Aristotelian opponents, yet making few converts. For his friend Cardinal Orsini he wrote out a new theory of the tides which, in his opinion, supplied decisive proof — *propaganda* may be closer to the truth[6] — for the Copernican system (the theory, of course, was wrong — it probably could not be otherwise, in the absence of a theory of gravitation). Orsini approached the Pope — Paul V, and was strongly rebuked. The Pope, who had the reputation of an anti-intellectual, and did not like what he knew of Galileo, consulted Bellarmine. The cardinal suggested that the two principal propositions of the Copernican astronomy be submitted for examination to the Holy See's board of theological qualifiers. This was done, and they ruled as follows:

1. That the sun is in the centre of the world, and totally immovable as to locomotion.
   Censure: All say that the said proposition is foolish and absurd in Philosophy, and formally heretical inasmuch as it contradicts the express opinion of Holy Scriptures in many places, according to the words themselves and according to the common expositions and meanings of the Church Fathers and doctors of theology.
2. That the earth is neither in the centre of the world nor immovable but moves as a whole and in daily motion.
   Censure: All say this proposition receives the same censure in Philosophy, and with regard to Theological verity it is at least erroneous in the faith.[5]

Galileo may not have expected this. He simply had not believed that the Church would be so foolish as to make an article of faith out of a scientific question . . .

Following complicated, Byzantine manoeuvres by various cardinals and Inquisitors, Galileo was officially enjoined not to 'hold, defend or teach in any way' the above propositions. A document was drawn up to this effect, *but was left unsigned*. At a meeting with the Inquisition, forewarned by Bellarmine that any other course would spell disaster, Galileo acquiesced. But he also had the foresight to obtain from Bellarmine a *signed* affidavit stating that whereas he was enjoined from teaching the Copernican theory as truth, he could continue using it as a working hypothesis. Foscarini's and Copernicus' books were put on the *Index* and Galileo returned to Florence, to resume — for a while — his long and oft interrupted work on motion. Unfortunately this was not to be the end of the story.

In 1618 three comets appeared in the night sky. Again Galileo found himself embattled. After talks and lectures — by him and by supporters — a Jesuit writing under the name of Sarsi accused him of surreptitiously upholding Copernicanism. He defended himself (1623) with the publication of *The Assayer* (*Il Saggiatore*) in which he took the Aristotelians to task:

> In Sarsi I seem to discern the firm belief that in philosophising one must support oneself on the opinion of some celebrated author, as if our minds ought to remain completely sterile and barren unless wedded to the reasoning of someone else. Possibly he thinks that philosophy is a book of fiction by some author, like the *Iliad* or *Orlando Furioso* — productions in which the least important thing is whether what is written in them is true. Well, Sarsi, that is not how things are. Philosophy is written in this grand book the universe, which stands continually open to our gaze. But the book cannot be understood unless one first learns to comprehend the language and to read the alphabet in which it is composed. It is written in the language of mathematics, and its characters are triangles, circles, and other geometric figures, without which it is humanly impossible to understand a single word of it; without these, one wanders about in a dark labyrinth.

The Assayer also discusses the difference between primary and secondary characteristics of matter — suggesting that it is the individual motions, i.e., the mechanical properties, of particles which determine the effect of matter upon our senses (colour, taste, etc.,). Such atomistic views, soon to be revived in France by Gassendi, were also a direct attack upon Aristotle.

In 1624 the embattled Galileo appeared to have a stroke of

luck: Pope Paul V died and was replaced by an old friend and admirer: Mafeo Barberini, who became Urban VIII. The friendship between the two men is described amusingly by Koestler as a relationship between two inflated egos, and the period 1624-30 as 'A kind of second honeymoon between the repository of Faith and the foremost representative of Science in Italy';[2] he remarks wryly that both considered themselves supermen — an unstable kind of relationship which, not surprisingly, had an explosive ending.

On a visit to Rome Galileo obtained the Pope's permission to publish his theory of tides. The result was his famous *Dialogue Concerning the Two Chief Systems of the World* — a title seemingly suggested by the Pope himself (who had not read the manuscript in its final form). The Copernican and Ptolemaic-Aristotelian theories are presented here as a three-cornered dialogue between Salviati (Galileo's mouthpiece), Sagredo (a friend) and Simplicio (an Aristotelian). Galileo's polemical talents are displayed here to the full. The clarity and astuteness of this exposition has few equals in the history of scientific literature. But it could never be reconciled with the 1616 order of the Inquisition in no way to 'hold, defend or teach' the Copernican system. He was not following Bellarmine's admonition to use the theory only as a hypothesis; and, to those who disagreed with him, he was at his arrogant best:

> It seems to me that we can have little regard for imbeciles who take it as a conclusive proof in confirmation of the Earth's motionlessness, holding them firmly in this belief, when they observe that they cannot dine today at Constantinople and sup in Japan, or those who are positive that the Earth is too heavy to climb over the sun and then fall headlong back again . . . Besides, with all the proofs in the world what would you expect to accomplish in the minds of people who are too stupid to recognise their own limitations?[7]

Elsewhere he refers to the Aristotelians as 'mental pygmies' and 'dumb idiots'.

The book appeared in Florence in March 1632; because of an outbreak of the plague it did not reach Rome until summer. But in August the Roman Inquisition, acting under instructions from a furious Pope banned its sales and ordered all sold copies to be bought back. Despite his advanced years and ill health, Galileo was told to come to Rome immediately or be brought in chains. Clearly, he had not expected this; what had gone wrong?

He had, at the very least, misjudged the tolerance of his friends within the Church — including Urban VIII. But more was involved. Stillman Drake feels that Galileo was too astute to commit so simple a blunder, too worldly to have deliberately courted danger over a matter of principle. The crux of the matter, according to Drake, appears to have been the unsigned 1616 document, still in the Inquisition files. *Someone*, most likely Galileo's old foe Scheiner, brought it to the attention of Urban VIII — who concluded that not only had a legal order of the Inquisition been disobeyed but also that he, the Pope, had been made to look a fool. A contributory cause may have been that Urban recognized some of his own arguments in the mouth of Simplicio and, being a vain man, had felt deeply humiliated — Renaissance popes did not like having rude noises made at them.[2]

The affair would have been even more serious had it not been for Bellarmine's 1616 affidavit, which Galileo produced as evidence of his good faith. Of the two principal documents of the trial this was the only signed one: Galileo's evidence was the best. The case, at this stage, should have been dismissed. But — and this he could not have foreseen — the Church was now in a box: it could not acquit him without losing face and damaging its authority. Galileo may have been too clever. What happened next is not certain. Perhaps Galileo panicked and threw himself at the mercy of the court. Or (Drake) there could have been some behind-the-scenes plea bargaining. Finally, it was agreed that if Galileo acknowledged in writing that the *Dialogue*, in places, overstepped allowable limits, his punishment would be light.

A different theory has been adduced recently by Pietro Redondi,[8] who suggests that Galileo's trial may have been a ruse to shield him from the more dangerous charge of heresy (for which he could have been put to death). Such an accusation could have been made on the basis of an unsigned document (initialled G) in the Vatican files attacking

Galileo's atomism (in *The Assayer*): immutable atoms implied the impossibility of transubstantiation — the bread and wine of the Communion could *not* be literally transformed into Christ's flesh and blood — wherefore the heresy. In this Redondi sees the hand of the Jesuits. Galileo's friends, and the Pope in particular, had no choice but to push through a trial on grounds of violating the 1616 injunction, to pre-empt one on far graver charges. Another Galileo scholar, Joseph Pitt, thinks that Redondi is pushing the evidence of a single document too far.[9] However this may be, it seems that another intriguing item has been fished out of these muddy waters.

Whatever the sequence of events, Galileo effectively received a life sentence. The conditions of detention, however, were not harsh. He never spent a day in jail, and he began his detention with four weeks in a comfortable flat in the Vatican, with valet and the Tuscan ambassador's *major domo* in attendance to see to his food and wine. Then he moved into the custody of a friend, the Archbishop Piccolamini of Siena. Later he was allowed to stay in his own home, under the watchful but apparently benign eye of emissaries from the Inquisition. Galileo lived out his last years at his villa in Arcetri, near the convent to which his daughter Virginia had retired in 1616. She died in 1634 — an emotional blow which almost killed the old man. But he was tough, and lived on in Arcetri and Florence for another eight years.

It was then that he wrote and published his greatest work: the *Discourse on Two New Sciences* — which appeared in print in 1638. This contained a full account of his thoughts, theorems and experiments on motion *plus* the foundation of a new science of the strength of materials. Had it not been for Galileo's involvement in the Copernican controversy this work, no doubt, would have been finished long before. It is an extraordinary tribute to Galileo's powers — unique in the annals of science — that, at the age of seventy-four, ill, almost blind, emotionally buffeted, he could still produce his *magnum opus* — a work ushering the era of modern Western science.

The *Discorsi* is the first modern treatment of uniformly accelerated motion — the theory of free fall and composite motions like the parabolic flight of a projectile. Gone are the fitful motions of Aristotelian mechanics, the broken curves of medieval ballistics, the circumvoluted reasoning of the 'philosophers'. It is all there — direct, lucid, basically simple and carefully explained; the arguments are still used in today's introductory mechanics texts. Too often, to the modern student, this material appears unbearably dull — the historical adventure, the excitement of discovery, the inspiration have long been filtered out — the sense of wonder is gone. Yet Galileo's ingenuity is a thing to marvel at. Take his classic free-fall experiments. Things dropped from a tower, or a table, fall very fast indeed — hundredths of a second must be measured to make sense of the data. Galileo recognized this; he knew also that he had no way of making such accurate observations — neither the experimenter's reflexes nor existing time-pieces were good enough. So he turned the problem around: he slowed down the phenomenon. He let objects fall, or roll, down a shallow sloping plane; the effective force was reduced to its component along the plane — gravity was diluted and the motion slowed enough to be measured by a crude water-clock!

Galileo was not merely clever; he was revolutionary. Others before him had come up with modern insights into the nature of science — Grosseteste, Roger Bacon, Buridan, Regiomontanus had made important statements on the role of observation, on the suspect nature of final causes and Aristotelian edicts. Galileo did much more. Not only did he excise most scholastic preconceptions from his work, he also stripped his models of unnecessary complications like friction or other 'small' effects. Archimedes had displayed a similar talent for abstraction, with his massless, perfectly rigid levers. But Galileo was the first to see clearly, and in its full generality, the role of imperfections and error in physics:

> I admit that the conclusions demonstrated in the abstract are altered in the concrete . . . But if such minutiae had to be taken into account in practical operations, we should have to commence by reprehending architects, who imagine that with plumb-lines they erect the highest towers in parallel lines (though these converge at the centre of the Earth).[10]

His essentially modern mind saw also what this implied:

> There is no event in Nature, not even the least that exists, that
> will ever be completely understood by theorists.[7]

But if you are careful and your judgment is good, you can remove unnecessary complexities from your model of nature and arrive at the core phenomena: *laws*, albeit approximate ones, are what science is about. This, says Galileo, has nothing to do with Aristotelian essences, perfection or final causes.

The Aristotelian and Platonic inheritances had been a burden — for two thousand years they had slowed the advance of Western science. Galileo marked an end to this; he, more than anyone, destroyed the comfortable scholastic environment of *the professors*.

After 1632 Galileo was forbidden to publish anything. The manuscript of the *Discorsi* was smuggled to Holland where it was printed in 1638 in Leyden by Elzevir. By the time it appeared, Galileo was blind. He was allowed to move to Florence to live with his son — as Jacob Bronowski has opined, Galileo had rather more children than a bachelor should.[11] He was forbidden to leave the house or converse with others.

Towards the end of his life, as his eyesight grew dim, he would scribble in the margin of his copy of the *Dialogues*. Some of his thoughts still call out to us today:

> In the matter of introducing novelties. And who can doubt that
> it will lead to the worst disorders when minds created free by
> God are compelled to submit slavishly to an outside will? When
> we are told to deny our senses and subject them to the whim
> of others? When people devoid of whatsoever competence are
> made judges over experts and are granted authority to treat
> them as they please? These are the novelties which are apt to
> bring about the ruin of commonwealths and the subversion of
> the state.

This cry from the heart of a great man is profoundly touching. It reminds us that, while knowledge has evolved at an explosive rate, values change but slowly. What Galileo says here can still be considered subversive — more obviously so in some places, perhaps, but still, to a degree, anywhere. The venue and the parties have changed — the cross-currents of history have seen to that. But the danger is the same; and our powers, both to seek *and* to supress knowledge are vastly greater than any Galileo dreamt of.

He died in Arcetri on 9th January 1642 — the year in which Newton was born.

CHAPTER TEN

Newton and the Enlightenment

Isaac Newton is buried in Westminster Abbey, amidst other great figures of British history. His tombstone, a slab of black marble flush with the floor, is trodden on by unnumbered thousands from all corners of the Earth. Above it his effigy has a place of pride in the great gilded choir screen of the nave. The neo-classical monument shows him recumbent, his elbow on four marble volumes; next to him, brandishing emblems of his work are two bemused cherubs; above is a weeping Astronomy — a classically attired lady sitting on a globe. Behind the effigy one glimpses bits of the old stone choir screen, painted black, now masked by the reds, blues and yellows of the brilliantly gilded 1832 version. The net effect is prodigal rather than beautiful; it embodies the awe in which Newton's name was held by his contemporaries and by later generations. And it is true, as one recent biographer has concluded, that only hyperbole can express the reality of this man's mind. For as long as the human race has a memory of things past Newton's name will shine, like a morning star, at the dawn of the scientific revolution.

Newton is our most famous man of science, an ornament of seventeenth and eighteenth century British and European intellectual life, the hero of Enlightenment philosophers and perhaps the supreme example of an individual's influence on the course of Western science and thought. Had he not lived his great insights — universal gravitation, the laws of mechanics, the dispersion of light — would doubtless have been duplicated, sooner or later; some, like the calculus, were in fact discovered independently by contemporaries. As is often the case, Newton's inspired ideas were the fruit of a period, of a cultural *ambiance*. But his genius provided a focus and a stimulus; the virtuoso performance of this one man

161

electrified the philosophers and scientists of his and succeeding generations. Had he died in infancy the development of science would surely have been slowed. And die he almost did — in the first week of his life.

Newton was born on Christmas day of 1642 in Woolsthorpe by Colsterworth in Lincolnshire; but, as someone once remarked, there is no record that wise men honoured the occasion. He was a diminutive and sickly infant — for the first week of his life his own mother did not expect him to live. His father, a successful farmer, had died three months before. When young Isaac was three his mother Hannah Newton, née Ayscough, married one Barnabas Smith, rector of Witham, who did not want the boy around. And so, until the rector's death in 1653, young Isaac lived with his maternal grandmother. While Hannah's marriage bettered the family fortunes, it deprived him of a mother and can have done little for his spirit. More than one scholar has conjectured that Newton's neurotic insecurity in later years, the inner anger which became visible in middle age, stemmed from the anguish of an abandoned child.

At the age of twelve the boy was packed off to grammar school where he studied Latin, Greek and the Bible. Obviously gifted above the average, he was unpopular with the other boys and, once or twice got into fights; only a passion for mechanical contrivances and sundials bespoke of his future avocation. He showed neither interest nor propensity for farming. At the insistence of a clear-minded headmaster (a Mr. Stokes) and an uncle (the Revd William Ayscough), he was sent up to Cambridge. Here he found awaiting him priceless treasures and a new life.

The Cambridge of 1662, already four hundred years old, was an odd place — a reservoir of patronage, an Anglican institution which, having weathered the Civil War, was adapting successfully to the Restoration, intellectually out of touch with the ferment on the continent and a degree mill for the ambitious. On the other hand, for those who, like Isaac Newton, arrived with a real thirst for study, it offered a unique repository of knowledge and books.

Newton began life at Trinity College as a *subsizar* i.e., as the poorest of the poor students, earning his keep with menial work

— like emptying the fellows' chamberpots. Considering that his mother could afford to support him in better style, this was hardly an uplifting start. But he was assiduous, solitary, an avid and judicious reader, and quickly discovered the magnificent world of scholarship — a world which claimed him for the next forty years.

After a brief exposure to Aristotelian physics and to the (then) rather feeble requirements of the standard curriculum, he set to digesting existing knowledge in mathematics and natural philosophy, both of which were in a state of rapid and exciting change. The researches of Wallis (1616-1703), Savilian professor at Oxford, and of the great Frenchman Fermat (1601-65) — preoccupied, among other things, with slopes and lengths of curves, areas and volumes — had brought mathematics to the brink of the calculus. Fermat, together with Descartes, had erected the discipline of analytic geometry — without which much, perhaps most, of modern science and mathematics are difficult to conceive. Robert Boyle (1627-91) was fathering chemistry and the physics of gases and in France Gassendi (1592-1655) had revitalized atomism, suggesting that atoms were small particles with mass and inertia, moving in a vacuum. Having also read Galileo's *Discorsi*, Newton became converted to the *Mechanical Philosophy*. He assimilated Descartes' writings, wherein he found much with which to agree — such as a preliminary formulation of the laws of motion, which he would adopt, improve and make his own. He also found much that was unpalatable — like the vortex-filled plenum its author used to explain the behaviour of the solar system. Newton left extensive notes, from which one sees that within six months of beginning to read mathematics he was making original alterations to the material. Within a year he had mastered all the extant literature and was sailing in uncharted waters. His readings in natural philosophy, optics and mechanics followed a similar pattern. By 1664 he obtained a scholarship, ceased to be a sizar, and threw himself into his work with total enthusiasm and concentration.

In the summer of 1665 Cambridge was 'visited with the plague of pestilence'. Excepting a brief interlude in the spring of 1666 when it had been prematurely concluded that the visitation was over, the university remained shut for almost two years — until the spring of 1667. Newton spent most of that time in Woolsthorpe. The story has it that here, in the peace and quiet of rural England, while the plague ravaged the towns, whilst the king fled from his capital and London burned, Newton reflected on the great problems in mathematics, physics and astronomy. These, according to his reminiscences of fifty years later, were his *anni mirabiles*.

It was then that he put down the foundations of his theory of fluxions (the calculus), discovered the binomial theorem, understood the theory of colours and conceived the role of gravity and the inverse square law in determining the motion of planets:[1]

> For in those days I was in the prime of my age for inventions & minded Mathematicks and Philosophy more than at any time since.

In his biography Westfall suggests that, most likely, Newton had taken critical steps towards the calculus and the theory of colours *before* the summer of 1665.[1] The famous anecdote of the falling apple leading to his flash of insight into the nature of gravitation, while containing a nugget of truth, is not wholly convincing — although it did occur to him, about then, that the force making the apple fall must be the same as that guiding the moon in its roughly circular orbit. Either during those two years, or shortly after, using a simple calculation balancing the centrifugal force on the moon with the Earth's attraction, Newton discovered that Kepler's relations led to an inverse square law for gravity. And, as he put it twenty years later, he found the forces of the Earth's gravity on the moon and on the apple to 'answer pretty well'.

Newton was extremely sensitive to questions of priority, yet he was always unconscionably slow to publish. His calculus appeared in print forty years after he 'had entrance into ye inverse method of fluxions' — a delay which would involve him in a bitter, distasteful battle over priorities with Leibniz who, meanwhile, discovered it independently. Newton's life-long reluctance to publish was not due to excessive modesty, nor to carelessness regarding priorities, but to a paranoiac fear of controversy *and* an obsession with rigour. This is awkward for historians, for it means that one has only an aging Newton's word for the chronology of his early work. It is most likely that he only cast the basic laws of motion in their final and correct form in 1684-85 in his *De Motu*. The development of his differential and integral calculus, while probably complete by 1690, was not published until 1704. The legend of the Woolsthorpe *anni mirabiles*, beautiful though it may be, is not wholly tenable — not, that is, in those versions which imply that his great discoveries, the beautiful intellectual structures which changed the face of science, sprang into being fully formed in 1665-66.

In 1669 Newton's Cambridge mentor, Isaac Barrow, resigned the Lucasian chair of mathematics. Newton took it over, lecturing in optics to a very sparse collection of students; apparently he was not an inspiring teacher. It was then that he conceived and built the first reflection telescope, a forerunner of today's giants, such as the one at Mount Palomar. He was elected to the Royal Society and submitted, in 1672, a paper on optics in which he proved, in a classic experiment with prisms, that white light consists of a superposition of coloured spectral components: glass refracts different parts of the spectrum differently, which is why a prism *disperses* light into its components. This kind of dispersion, thought Newton, was inevitable in lenses and imposed absolute limitations in the design of ordinary telescopes. This is actually not the case, yet from this he drew an eminently practical result: since light is not dispersed on reflection, he used a mirror to collect it. His views on the chromatic constitution of light, which were largely correct, were at variance with those of his contemporaries, and he was immediately attacked by a variety of critics, most of whom he demolished rather easily. But Robert Hooke was another matter. A first-rate man and the leading English authority on optics, he subscribed to the idea that colours were not intrinsic components of white light, but were the result of its modification by the glass. The resulting debate, lengthy and acrimonious, was followed by lasting enmity. Said Newton a few years later, confiding to Leibniz (before falling out with him):[1]

> I was so persecuted with discussions arising from the publication of my theory of light, that I blamed my own imprudence for parting with so substantial a blessing as my quiet to run after a shadow.

In subsequent years Newton all but abandoned science and mathematics. It is an arresting thought — and an embarrassment to the Royal Society — that Newton's scientific work constitutes only about ten per cent of his life-long intellectual output, most of which was given to *theology* and *alchemy*. His erudition in these fields appears to have been impressive. Contemporary theologians have testified that his knowledge and understanding of the Scriptures and the hermeneutic writings was second to none.

Newton's theological readings led him to unorthodox conclusions. He came to believe that the introduction of Trinitarianism had been a deliberate fraud, which he traced to Athanasius in the fourth century — a corruption of Christianity and a 'fals infernal religion'. Newton, in other words, became an Arian — a follower of Arius — believing in a *single*, all-pervasive, ubiquitous God. From the Anglican (and Roman Catholic) standpoint this was heresy, and to preserve his Cambridge position Newton had to keep this, his innermost religious conviction, a secret. This was neither cowardice nor paranoia, but simple discretion and good sense.

As for Newton's fascination with alchemy, it began, it seems, with an interest in chemistry (one finds, in his early notebooks, a recipe for making phosphorus which begins with the valiant instruction: 'Take of urine one barrel . . .'). But alchemy must have struck him as more profound[1] and he thereby entered another, at least in part clandestine, field of thought. Again he mastered a huge mass of writings, copying rare manuscripts in his own hand, making numerous annotations. As in his theological wanderings, he felt that here he was exploring the really deep problems of life and philosophy; it was a search for truth — and, judging from the enormous amounts of time he spent on it, for much of his life he found alchemy considerably more interesting than mathematics. He spent months concocting strange experiments, forgetting to eat and sometimes to sleep. This may have had unfortunate results for his health: he made generous use of mercury compounds, and modern analyses of his hair have shown abnormally high levels thereof. A degree of mercury poisoning may well explain some strange incidents in his middle years.

For ten years, between 1670 and the early 1680s, Newton worked almost exclusively on alchemy and theology. He reduced his scientific correspondence to a trickle and did his level best to abandon natural philosophy and mathematics. In this he nearly succeeded, and his greatest works might never have been born but for continued intrusions into his life of scientific colleagues and friends. The scientific ferment of the times was so strong, and his reputation already so great, that Newton was simply not allowed to disappear into the quiet anonymity of his academic sanctum to carry on, as he would have liked, his shadowy alchemical and theological pursuits.

The most burning questions in science were still astronomical ones, and the Astronomer Royal, John Flamsteed, came to consult Newton about the great comets of 1681 and 1682. And in August 1684 the astronomer Edmund Halley came to visit and to ask a question which he felt Newton alone could answer.

The story of this momentous exchange has been recounted by Abraham de Moivre from Newton's own recollection:[1]

> In 1684 Dr Halley came to visit him at Cambridge, after they had been some time together, the Dr asked him what he thought the Curve would be that would be described by the Planets supposing the force of attraction towards the Sun to be reciprocal to the square of their distance from it. Sr. Isaac replied immediately that it would be an Ellipsis, the Doctor struck with joy & amazement asked him how he knew it, why saith he I have calculated it, whereupon Dr Halley asked him for his calculation without any further delay, Sr. Isaac looked among his papers but could not find it, but he promised him to renew it, & then to send it him . . .

But when Newton finally laid hands upon the paper and tried to repeat the old demonstration, he discovered a mistake. He had to re-derive the result from scratch. In November he sent Halley a nine-page article entitled *De Motu Corporum in Gyrum* (on the motion of bodies in an orbit). This contained, for the first time, a sketch of Newton's universal theory of gravitation and of his mechanics. Halley, recognizing its importance, insisted on registering the copy with the secretary of the Royal Society. Newton was now enthralled by his new method, by the idea of universal gravitation and the intellectual vistas opening up before him. He set to work on what would, in 1685, become the first volume of the *Philosophiae Naturalis Principia Mathematica* — the famous *Principia* which, published in 1687, is arguably the most influential scientific work of all time.

The *Principia* contained the foundations of classical physical theory for future centuries, enunciating the laws of motion that bear Newton's name, as well as those of universal gravitational attraction. Newton's first law states that a body not subject to a force must travel at constant speed along a straight line. The second says that if a force is applied to a body, its momentum increases in the direction of the force: for a body of unchanging mass, the resulting rate of increasing speed, or acceleration, is equal to the force divided by the mass. While for the proper formulation of these laws Newton had his own method of fluxions and inverse fluxions i.e., the differential and integral calculus, for the *Principia* he recast his discussions into geometrical terms — an intellectual oddity which has been much discussed, and which seems to reflect his aesthetic preference for the methods of classical geometry. Newton's third law stated that to every action there corresponds an equal but opposite reaction: forces exerted on each other by two bodies — such as two planets — are equal but opposite. The law of gravitation says further that two spheres, like the sun and the earth, exert upon each other forces of attraction that vary inversely with the square of the distance between their centers. The combination of these simple axioms led to a model for the solar system: planets in elliptical orbits with the sun at a focus, moons in similar orbits about their planets, all of it predictable, it seemed, with perfect accuracy — Kepler's laws following, ineluctably, from the mathematics. This marked the birth of theoretical dynamics and of modern classical physics; until the beginning of the twentieth century Newton's laws were to reign supreme in man's view of the cosmos. In fact they never have been superseded; it is only outside certain limits, in dealing with the very large at one end and the very small at the other, that they have been replaced by more fundamental viewpoints. Many astronomical phenomena and most of geophysics, much of our ongoing technological activity, can be adequately understood in Newtonian terms: the Apollo moonflights and the Mars landings are examples of Newton's laws at work. The *Principia* contain many other riches; the basis of wave theory, and of fluid mechanics; the theory of motion in a resisting medium; the precession of the equinoxes and a theory of the tides; any one of these achievements would have earned him recognition as the outstanding physicist of his day. Taken together they represent an incredible monument to human genius. Men like Newton are not of the same cloth as the rest of us.

The birth of the *Principia* was not without the sort of pain and controversy Newton hated most; once again he was confronted by Hooke who maintained that he had thought of the inverse square law before Newton, and accused him of plagiarism. The masterpiece clearly cost Newton a gigantic effort, and while he continued to write and publish, he henceforth did little original work.

His mother having died in 1679 Newton had, for a while, no close attachments. His interest in women was slight, or possibly non-existent. During the 1680s he made several new friends. The Dutchman Christiaan Huygens came to visit him, and the philosopher John Locke became an intellectual confidant. In 1689 he was elected member of parliament for Cambridge, but did not leave much of a mark. He seems to have voted with the majority on most issues — as in the motion to uphold the deposition of James and to tender the crown to William and Mary (1690). It was then, or thereabouts, that he met a young Swiss, Fatio de Duillier. Fatio was twenty-five and a fine mathematician; Newton and Fatio took an immediate liking for each other. For four years their friendship flourished. This, says Westfall, was the most meaningful emotional relationship in Newton's life. It was broken off abruptly after the two men had met in London in early 1693. The sudden dissolution of a relationship that had meant a great deal to both parties remains unexplained. Most likely it was but a symptom of the general breakdown Newton suffered during that year — an attack of depression and paranoia which made him suspect everyone. He wrote strange accusatory letters confessing guiltily to Locke that he had had 'uncharitable thoughts' and had suspected him of trying to embroil him with women. In a letter to Samuel Pepys he said that he 'must withdraw from your acquaintance'. Locke and Pepys, being intelligent, discrete men of the world, forgave and forgot. But initially these goings-on led to rumours abroad in particular where, for a time, it was said that Newton was 'so disturbed in mind . . . as to be reduced to very ill circumstance' (Huygens). Whatever the cause of Newton's disorder, whether the result of overwork on a neurotic personality, or of mercury poisoning, he pulled out of it — completely, it seems. In 1697 he solved with ease a mathematical challenge problem sent to him by Bernouilli and Leibniz — a triumph, but one mixed with exasperation; as he would put it someday: 'I do not love . . . to be dunned & teezed by foreigners about mathematical things.'

His later years were affluent and filled with adulation. In 1696 he became Warden and, in 1699, Master of the Mint — posts he filled conscientiously and well; indeed, he seems to have pursued counterfeiters mercilessly and with zest. In 1703, following Hooke's death, Newton was elected president of the Royal Society — a society which had by then lost its early lustre and enthusiasm.

In 1704 Newton published his *Opticks* — an impressive presentation of work completed more than thirty years before. Helpful in fathoming Newton's philosophy of nature are the Queries which conclude the book. These show that he believed all matter and light to consist of particles interacting through short-range forces of far greater magnitude than those of gravity. He understood that bodies act on light 'emitting, reflecting, refracting and inflecting it' and, conversely, that 'light (acts) upon bodies for heating them and putting their parts into a vibrating motion wherein heat consists'. In one version he expressed the opinion that infinite space is the 'Sensorium of a Being incorporeal, living and intelligent, who sees things themselves intimately, and thoroughly perceives them, and comprehends them wholly by their immediate presence to himself.' He quickly got cold feet and tried to recall all copies of this edition, to eliminate the word Sensorium. But an uncorrected copy got to Leibniz, who held up this passage to scathing ridicule.

Relations with Leibniz had been deteriorating — the calculus priority question had been simmering for decades. It became vitriolic when, after the second edition of the *Principia* (1709), Leibniz wrote a protesting letter to Hans Sloane, secretary of the Royal Society. Those who have studied the massive literature believe that Leibniz's claim to independent discovery is indisputable. Newton's error was in having delayed publication for too long.

Neither scholarly nor pretty, the quarrel dragged on for years. Perhaps the less said about it, the better — it was an unedifying picture: two aging giants jealous of each other, going at it hammer and tongs. Had Newton been younger and more firmly in control, things may never have turned as ugly as they did. It all ended only with Leibniz's death in 1716, at the age of seventy.

A third edition of the *Principia* appeared in 1723. But in these later years, Newton's intellectual powers had waned and his memory became erratic. However, he maintained his connection with the Mint, and with the Royal Society. A rich man by then, he was also extremely generous to a multitude of less fortunate relatives. At least one biographer, contemplating Newton's astonishing list of charities, has commented that he has, thereby, atoned handsomely for his less than generous squabbles with Leibniz and Hooke . . .

Reminiscing over his life, some months before his death in March 1726, he offered this famous and magnificent vignette of himself:

> I don't know what I may seem to world, but, as to myself, I seem to have been only like a boy playing on the sea shore, and diverting myself in now and then finding a smoother pebble or a prettier shell than ordinary, whilst the greater ocean of truth lay all undiscovered before me.

Newton's influence on society extended far beyond the confines of science. It was to permeate Western civilization's view of the world — its philosophy, politics, ethics. It marked the coming of age of Western science and ushered the industrial era. Newton had shown that one could *understand* the universe

— light, the motion of bodies, the heavens themselves behaved in comprehensible ways. Simple, powerful laws seemed to explain the motion of the planets — the riddle of the heavens, the problem of natural philosophy which, since prehistoric times, had concerned humanity the most. It was our first blueprint of the universe — or at least of a corner thereof; and it was drawn with an economy of principle and an accuracy undreamt of by previous generations. Where once there had been a kind of intellectual chaos, there appeared order and light — the possibility, it seemed, of explaining and predicting the motions of planets, moons and comets with delicate precision into an indefinite future. Newton concluded an era — millenia during which humanity had fumbled its way to a rational world model; and he demonstrated that this could be done in simple mechanistic terms. He had shown the way, completing the intellectual revolution begun by Galileo — a revolution which accomplished 'the eclipse of scholastic philosophy (and) the destruction of Aristotelian physics' and 'outshines everything since the rise of Christianity and reduces the Renaissance and Reformation to the rank of mere episodes, mere internal displacements within the system of medieval Christiandom' (Herbert Butterfield [2]).

Thus began an age of philosophical optimism unparalleled since the Golden age of Greece: if the intransigent problems of planetary motion could be so elegantly resolved, why not others — like all the social, economic, political and ethical questions that had plagued civilisation for so long! Late seventeenth and eighteenth century thinkers — Locke, Hume, Adam Smith in Britain and the French *Philosophes* (Diderot, d'Alembert, Fontenelle) — were all optimists; they tried to do for these other fields of thought what Newton had done for physics. Even Voltaire, writing with Madame du Chatelet, gave a popular account of Newton's *Principia*. D'Alembert, in his *History of the Sciences*, exults: 'Newton . . . gave philosophy a form which apparently it is to keep.'

The eighteenth century saw also the burgeoning of many kinds of machinery; with philosophical enthusiasm came the dawn of the *Industrial Revolution*. There were dissenting voices — like Rousseau's — but, on the whole, the tone was set by the *Philosophes* — as in Diderot's article on *The Stocking Machine*:[3]

The stocking-loom is one of the most complicated and the most rational and ingenious of all machines; one can regard it as one single and prolonged act of reason, of which the manufactured article is the logical conclusion . . .

Fulfilling Bacon's prophesy, humanity had made the connection between celestial mechanics and machinery — between the heavens and its stockinged feet; an *act of reason* was the link.

Isaiah Berlin summed up the times in these words:[4]

The intellectual power, honesty, lucidity, courage and disinterested love of the truth of the most gifted thinkers of the eighteenth century remain to this day without parallel. Their age is one of the best and most hopeful episodes in the life of mankind.

This was *the Enlightenment*. Science was to be its tool, Newton its prophet.

For a long time thereafter science, philosophy and economics emulated Newton. But two important points remained unnoticed. The first was that, however remarkable Newton's achievement, the problems of planetary motion were simple compared to the everyday conundrums of society, of politics, or even of the natural sciences. The second was that Newton had *not* bequeathed us a method — no more than, say, Rembrandt has left us a recipe for turning out great art. Our modern philosophers, indeed, no longer believe there is such a thing as *the* scientific method. These misunderstandings were important, deep, and were to colour much of Western thought for the next two hundred years.

On a more immediate, workaday scale Newton also contributed to technological developments — indirectly, through the endless ramifications of his theory of mechanics, and directly through personal intervention. An example of direct influence was his role in the search for a technique of measuring longitude at sea.

In the eighteenth century sailing ships plied the oceans in pursuit of colonial riches, power and new routes. Circumnavigating the planet, exploring remote corners of the Pacific, they spent months or years at sea. Nevertheless, their navigation was haphazard. A ship's officer could, with reasonable accuracy, deduce latitude from the sun's height at noon, but had no reliable means of determining longitude; errors of a hundred miles or more in estimated position at the end of a month's voyage were common. Lives, fleets, fortunes and admirals were lost through poor navigation and shipwreck. There was an urgent, obvious need for a method of measuring longitude and in 1714 Parliament convened a committee to examine the problem. Newton's advice was sought. He advised that a prize be established and Parliament passed a 'public reward for such person or persons as shall discover the Longitude'. Following Newton's suggestion the reward was graded according to the accuracy of the method — £20,000 for any device that would determine longitude to within 30' of arc (30 nautical miles at equatorial latitudes), £10,000 for 1°. These were considerable fortunes and Parliament created a Board of Longitude to keep an eye on the money and the flood of proposals that followed — many of which Newton was forced to deal with himself. It was a vexing problem; yet longitude is but a measure of the difference between local time and mean time somewhere else (for example between local noontime and that at Greenwich); one answer, then, was an accurate timepiece which could withstand the rigours of the sea — with, of course, a suitable instrument for 'shooting the sun'. This was understood; but the requirement for a clock that would, during a sea voyage of months, lose or gain no more than a couple of seconds a day, seemed beyond the state of the early eighteenth century clockmaker's art. The problem was solved a quarter century after Newton's death by John Harrison, a Yorkshire carpenter.[5]

Harrison had built his first clock in 1715, at the age of twenty-two, a grandfather clock with gears and wheels of oak. Upon hearing of the prize, he started work on a succession of increasingly accurate marine chronometers, in which he incorporated several revolutionary inventions: among these was an almost frictionless 'grasshopper' escapement and a clever method of compensating for temperature-induced length changes of the balance spring. In 1759, at the age of sixty-seven, after forty-five years of effort, he finished his famous Number Four. Too old for a long sea voyage, he sent it with his son, William Harrison, on a naval vessel from Portsmouth to Jamaica; on arrival, Number Four was five seconds slow, giving a total navigational error of a one and a quarter nautical miles: a remarkable achievement, even by twentieth century standards (only in recent decades, since the advent of satellite navigation, has it become possible to do consistently better). On the return trip, after a very rough crossing, a similar test gave an error of twenty-eight and a half minutes of longitude. So Harrison and son had clearly won the £20,000 . . . or so they thought. As long as Harrison had been working on the chronometer, the Board of Longitude had supported him with small grants. But now the official position was taken that the whole thing had been a fluke, and new sea trials were ordered; although these were successful the Board still refused to part with the money unless given the plans for the mechanism (1765). After Harrison complied, they gave him *half* the prize and ordered new chronometers and new trials; the Astronomer Royal, the Revd Maskelyne, who had a competing method of longitude determination was entrusted with some of the testing and, regretably, produced an unfavourable report. And so it went, an endless tale of chicanery and procrastination. In the meantime a French clockmaker, Pierre LeRoy, had also solved the problem with his chronometer, which was tested in 1763. In 1772 Harrison approached the king — George III — and enlisted his help; he also circulated a broadside against the Board; public indignation grew and Parliament intervened: the Yorkshire carpenter, now an old man with failing eyes and unsteady hands, finally collected the rest of his prize money in 1773.[5]

The saga of Harrison's chronometer shows how those entrusted with running society were already consciously and deliberately appealing to science and technology for the solution of practical problems. It is a classic example of the needs of a civilization giving rise to a whole technology and a new era of scientific instrumentation — in this case, an era of precise timekeeping. Accurate time-pieces were to be essential tools for scientists — astronomers, geophysicists, geographers or laboratory physicists. On solid land Harrison's *Number Four* and LeRoy's chronometers kept time to within one tenth of a second a day, i.e., to about one part in a million; they were the first true precision instruments for measuring time.

Newton's eighteenth century successors were many; even a simple unannotated list would be unconscionably long. A few household names in the world of science deserve special mention.

There were the *Bernouillis* from Switzerland — Jacques, John, Daniel and six others, a remarkable example of family talent distributed over several generations (a prime exhibit, with the Bachs and the Darwins, of all who take the side of 'nature' in the nature-nurture debate). Talented, competitive, jealous of each other, they fought even among themselves; after winning a French Academy award Daniel (1700-82) was thrown out of the house by his equally famous father John who had wanted the prize for himself. Apart from fanning the flames of the Leibniz-Newton calculus controversy, John Bernouilli (1667-1748) solved the problems of the line of swiftest descent and of the ray of light in a medium of varying index of refraction. Daniel's most famous work is his *Hydrodynamica*, wherein he offered the world the foundations of the kinetic theory of gases. This sees a gas as a huge number of corpuscles in continuous motion, colliding with each other and with the walls of the container; higher temperatures correspond to greater speeds, i.e. greater energy, of these particles; pressure is produced by their impact.

There was Leonhard Euler (1707-83), also Swiss, who spent a good part of his life in St Petersburg and who, apart from profound contributions to mathematics, formulated the equations of fluid motion which still bear his name. Other important mathematicians were the Frenchmen Lagrange (1736-1813) who reformulated Newtonian mechanics and put it into modern form, d'Alembert (1717-83) the Encyclopaedist, and Pierre Simon de Laplace (1749-1827).

Laplace's life is a curious one; it spans the most turbulent era in France's recent history. He rode the tides of change with an opportunism that smacked of political genius. He rose to high posts under Louis XVI, did well for himself during the Revolution, was made a count by Napoleon Bonaparte and, some years later, was awarded the title of marquis by Louis XVIII. He also occasionally stole ideas from others whom he failed to acknowledge.[6]

Laplace's work sits astride the eighteenth and nineteenth centuries and encompasses most of physics. One of his contributions was to solve a problem which had greatly worried Newton, concerning the stability of the solar system: he showed that small perturbations of the system remained small and would not lead to a collapse of the planetary orbits. Thus, whereas Newton had assumed that God intervened to keep the system running smoothly, Laplace, as he put it, had no need for this hypothesis. Laplace also derived and studied the famous potential equation, now named after him, describing the behaviour of gravitational, electrostatic and magnetostatic forces, of steady heat flows and ideal fluids — opening up rich areas of study for the nineteenth century. He produced a treatise on probability theory and a very sensible model of the origins of the solar system. The latter is known as the nebular hypothesis, and had been partly anticipated by Immanuel Kant in 1755; according to it the sun and the planets condensed from a rotating mass of gas. Our twentieth century view, which includes additional effects like hydrodynamic turbulence and magnetic fields, may be seen as an up-dating thereof.

Laplace it was, too, who best expressed the scientific faith of the Enlightenment and of the following century with his famous metaphor of the *Divine Calculator*. Were such a being to be endowed, at some instant, with a complete knowledge of the position and velocity of every particle of matter in the universe it would, according to Laplace, be able to predict the future with absolute accuracy. The power of knowledge is, ultimately, the power of prediction; and so knowledge and science found themselves equated to potentially unlimited power. Historically speaking, this must be the high point of our philosophical optimism.

Astronomy flourished: the systematic exploration of the large-scale universe properly began in the eighteenth century. It was chiefly a matter of improved tools (Newton, Huygens), more accurate time-pieces (Harrison, LeRoy), more powerful mathematical techniques. The stars were now seen as faraway suns. The Milky Way was understood to be an immense, flat, disk-like collection of distant starts (Thomas Wright, 1750). The grouping of stars into remote Milky Way-type structures (galaxies) was postulated by Kant. Sir William

Herschel (1738-1822) began his monumental sky surveys, which were to be continued into the nineteenth century by his son John. Sir William, who began his career as a musician, became famous as builder of magnificent Newtonian telescopes, with the help of which he revealed, in 1781, the existence of Uranus — the first planet to be *discovered* in recorded history!

During the second half of the eighteenth century headway was made in understanding electricity. Benjamin Franklin (1706-90) — he who, according to his epitaph, 'snatched lightning from the heavens and sceptres from kings', showed that lightning is electricity, that charge is conserved and that there is action-at-a-distance between charges. But it was Joseph Priestley (1733-1804) who, through a brilliant piece of deductive reasoning, first inferred that this takes place according to a law similar to Newtonian gravitation, i.e., with a force proportional to the inverse distance squared. In 1774 Cavendish (1731-1810) reached the same conclusion, and Mitchell (1724-93) showed that this held also for the force between magnetic poles. This basic law of action-at-a-distance was verified directly with a torsion balance by Coulomb (1738-1810) in France; it has since been known as Coulomb's law.

Chemistry, after its somewhat uncertain beginnings in alchemy and physics, began to develop rapidly in the latter half of the eighteenth century. Robert Boyle had been the first to conceive an embryonic idea of elements and chemical compounds. By the time of Lavoisier (1743-94) carbon, sulphur, phosphorous and all the metals were recognized as elements. The efforts of Scheele in Sweden, Priestley in England and Lavoisier in France established the existence of oxygen; the composition of air and water were understood; hydrogen was added to the list of elements. In his celebrated experiments on combustion, Lavoisier showed that whereas matter alters its state in chemical reactions, the total mass does not change. He thus introduced into science one of the great conservation laws: the *conservation of matter*, which was to play a central role in the development of chemistry.

For the twin sciences and arts of physiology and medicine the eighteenth century was a period of steady growth, during which efforts were made to explain various body functions in mechanical terms. Men like the Swiss Albrecht von Haller (1708-77) investigated the mechanisms of muscles, respiration, digestion and bone formation; so did the French naturalist Reamur (1683-1757) and the Italian Abbé Spallanzani (1729-99). Medicine's ability to prolong lives or alleviate suffering remained erratic. Indeed, it has been said that average life expectancy in the seventeenth century was somewhat less than in the sixteenth; however, to blame this on medical progress may be unsporting.

A major breakthrough came in the *earth sciences* when Hutton (1726-79) published his *Theory of the Earth* (1785), arguing that the processes which had shaped the Earth in the past were those that were still shaping it today. This *principle of uniformitarianism* was a step towards a modern geology; it was to help do away with creationist and catastrophist theories — or, at least, with the more simple-minded and traditionalist versions thereof. Hutton, an Edinburgh doctor, had, at one stage of his life, been involved in farming. It is said that he liked walking the countryside; that this led him to think carefully about the Earth; he saw that valleys were cut by rivers, and plains formed by the alluvial deposits they set down. Yet many an intelligent person had also farmed, walked the countryside and, presumably meditated on these matters; what seems like common sense to us today had been long in coming. But traditional myths and religion had, since the dawn of consciousness, militated in favour of divine interventions and arbitrary change. It is hard for us today to understand the difficulties experienced by an eighteenth century mind when confronted by mounting evidence for the enormous antiquity of the Earth, for past extinctions of species, or for the progression of life forms towards greater complexity through the eons . . .

Interestingly, the concept of evolution, dormant — for more than two thousand years — since the days of Anaximander and Xenophanes *c.* 500 BC — was reborn in the eighteenth century. The somewhat laboured mechanisms proposed by Charles Bonnet in France were followed by the end of the century by Lamarck's theory which proposed a continuous upward evolution from simple organisms to more complex and better adapted ones. Lamarck is therefore often regarded as the father of modern evolution. The major flaw in his model was the assumption of transmission of characteristics acquired by individuals during their lifetime; it is to this particular feature of the theory that the name of Lamarck has often been attached. And while Darwin's theory was to supplant it in the nineteenth century, Lamarckism retained sufficient appeal to have suffered periodic efforts at reinstauration. These, however, appear to have always foundered either due to imperfections of the data or, occasionally, fraud (Lysenko).

Humanity's view of the world was thus acquiring a modern cast. By the end of the eighteenth century science was ripe for an updated form of atomism. The cosmos had been enormously expanded; we were beginning to perceive our minuteness — our seeming unimportance in a vast universe people by billions of stars, each star a sun immeasurably more distant than our. Scientists could now cope in mathematically sophisticated ways with force and motion; the nineteenth century mechanistic outlook was crystallizing — the cosmos was a gigantic, accurate mechanism running in accordance with Newton's laws. But the general picture still had huge gaps. The laws of electromagnetism, as well as those of thermodynamics, had yet to be formulated; without them no scientific understanding of our world is conceivable. Geology was just emerging from its purely descriptive phase. In the biological sciences, facts were being accumulated with, as yet, no reliable models to weave them into systematic patterns; our capacity for self-analysis was still too undeveloped to give birth to disciplines yet to come, such as serious anthropology or psychology. One needs only to read Buffon's 1761 description of the American Indian to see how thin, still, was the veneer of Enlightenment objectivity; a Frenchman and a naturalist, this is how he put it:[7]

> In the savage, the organs of generation are small and feeble. He has no hair, no beard, no ardour for the female. Though nimbler than the European, because more accustomed to running, his strength is not so great. His sensations are less acute; and yet he is more timid and cowardly. He has no vivacity, no activity of the mind . . . It is easy to discover the cause of the

scattered life of savages, and of their estrangement from society. They have been refused the most precious spark of Nature's fire. They have no ardour for women and, of course, no love to mankind . . .

Perhaps the Enlightenment *Philosophes* no longer saw humanity as God's elect. Reason was replacing superstition . . . and, of course, Europeans, with their science and industry, believed themselves vastly superior to other races. The enthronement of Reason, in other words, had brought its own delusions. Most significant, perhaps, was the mirage of a world that was, in principle, fully predictable. Today, Buffon's naive anthropological fancies are dead; but illusions of potentially infinite power — albeit in modified form — are alive and well.

CHAPTER ELEVEN

The Age of Certainty

The dark satanic mills are long gone, yet much of Britain's manufacturing heartland remains a dreary place. Sprawling out and away from the great northern cities are miles of industrial landscape, monotonous, grey and unloved: power stations, cooling towers, factories, railway sidings. Here and there one finds dead tissue — disused canals, oily waters over black mud, grimy buildings, crumbling warehouses, deserted yards. Here, in this spent land, the barons made their fortunes, took their money and lived elsewhere . . .

Superficially, we have cleaned up our act — at home, that is. The more obvious excesses of the industrial revolution — the total absence of pollution control, destruction of the fabric of society, unconscionable exploitation of the poor — have, to some extent, been exported abroad. To witness these in full swing, to see a reconstruction of how *we* once operated, one must venture into the industrial suburbs of Third World cities, where millions live in squalor and misery, in shockingly polluted shanty towns, in the poisoned shade of factories, refineries and chemical plants which manufacture so many of our imports.

The industrial centres of nineteenth-century Europe, Britain and North America were hardly better. Profits were also their reason for being, and, of course, the growing power of machinery multiplied these spectacularly — first in the textile industry, then in other areas. Technology and inventiveness flourished, feeding back into science; as Bernal has stressed[1], the so-called industrial revolution was, in fact, an industrial-scientific revolution. In Britain, the Midlands were its cradle. Mechanization and the steam engine were its keystones. The theory — or, rather, the rationalization — was provided by Adam Smith with his ideas on the distribution of labour and the

183

invisible hand of capitalism. Colonies furnished ready captive markets to absorb the output and to create the wealth which, ultimately, stimulated interest in further technical advances. The brains for these were supplied by an alliance of engineers, scientists and manufacturers — people like Telford the bridge man, Brindley the canal-builder, Watt the instrument-maker, Wilkinson the ironmaster, Joseph Priestley the chemist . . .

By the end of the eighteenth century the interplay between science, philosophy, technology, economics, society, and the great French and American Revolutions, had become exceedingly complex. A relatively simple and explicit example of such interaction is the history of the steam engine, a commonly accepted — textbook — version of which runs as follows.[1,2]

In the fifteenth and sixteenth centuries the vanishing of British forests had led to rising firewood prices and, by the seventeenth, trade and industry were switching to coal as a preferred fuel. Then, as mining developed and shafts were sunk to increasing depths, the removal of water from mines became a serious problem. The old bucket-chains and suction pumps driven by wind and water mills, or by teams of horses, were erratic and not always suited to the terrain. And so heat energy was tried. The earliest steam-driven pump was that of Captain Thomas Savery, a Dartmouth engineer. It could lift a lot of water fast; but it was unwieldy and each pump was limited by atmospheric pressure to raising water to a maximum height of 30 feet (1698). Ten or so years later a Dartmouth blacksmith, Thomas Newcomen (1663-1729), encouraged by Robert Hooke, built an all-purpose steam engine — which, however, was to be useful largely in collieries and mines. John Smeaton (1724-92) further refined it through the study of models. But the Scottish instrument-maker and engineer James Watt (1736-1819) used scientific principles to improve engine performance. In this he followed the advice of Joseph Black (1728-99), physician and chemist, professor of medicine at the University of Glasgow, who had carefully thought out the concepts of specific and latent heats. Understanding this allowed Watt to step up efficiency by introducing a separate low-temperature condenser chamber, thus keeping the main cylinder from cooling between strokes, as it had in earlier versions. Also vital were new high-precision canon-boring techniques (Wilkinson's 1774 patent), allowing much finer cylinder tolerances and tighter fitting pistons.

Black had made the first infusion of pure science into steam engine design. Until then its development had been a matter of craftsmanship rather than science, of intuition rather than physics. The rest of the story is different. The very success of Watt's engine induced others to think about it and to wonder how its efficiency could be further improved. This, in turn, encouraged the birth of a new field of physics: the mechanics of heat or *thermodynamics*. But heat is *energy* and, as the discipline grew, its scope extended to *all* forms of energy. Not surprisingly, thermodynamics became a bulwark of modern physics and chemistry; today it even plays a central role in cosmology.

The father of this new discipline was Sadi Carnot (1796-1832), a French engineer who, stimulated by Watt's engine to think about efficiency, work, and energy availability, had come to some extremely interesting conclusions. Among other things, he proved that work can only be done by transferring heat between different temperatures. He was also the first to determine the mechanical equivalent of heat — the precise translation of calories into units of mechanical energy — but died of cholera before he could publish his results.[1] The credit for this discovery has usually been given to three people: Robert Mayer (1814-87) in Germany (a ship's doctor), Robert Prescott Joule (1818-89), an English scientist of independent means, and von Helmholtz (1821-94) in Germany (physiologist and physicist). This equivalence is an insight of profound significance: it demonstrates the *conservation of energy*. This, *the first law of thermodynamics* and one of the most far-reaching and powerful principles in science, says that whereas energy can be moved about between the various parts of an isolated system, as well as between different forms (thermal, electrical, mechanical, etc.,), its total amount stays constant. Clearly this deeply affects how we perceive the universe — and how we run our industrial and economic world.

Carnot also understood that what matters in practice is the availability of the energy — it is useless if you cannot get at it. This could be conveniently described by the concept of *entropy*, so named in 1850 by Clausius (1822-88) — a quantity defining the *unavailability* of the energy, which would also be shown to be a measure of the system's disorder (Boltzmann, 1844-1906).

The connection between disorder, entropy and energy availability is illustrated by engine parts strewn over a garage floor. You cannot extract work out of it — the system is too disordered: the availability of energy is low, the entropy is high. Put the parts together in their proper relationship, the system is now highly ordered, the entropy is low and you have a running engine: energy is easily available. Likewise the rusted hulk of some disused machine, or the shattered, vandalized clay tablets of Sumer and Babylon have higher entropy than when they were new.

The simplest concepts are often the most profound; entropy is no exception. It allows, in particular, a succinct statement of the *second law of thermodynamics* which says that the entropy of an isolated system must increase (or, more precisely, that it can never decrease — which, in most cases, amounts to the same thing).

The law is universal — on the macroscopic scale, at least, it holds everywhere and for all things. It seemed natural, then, to apply it to the world of stars and galaxies: the total energy in the universe may be constant but, as time goes by, it becomes less and less available. In twentieth century terminology, order is equivalent to information: increasing entropy implies, in general, decreasing information. In modern language, information will vanish — such was the message of the second law. Today we are less sure. We are no longer quite comfortable with the idea of 'the' universe as an isolated system.[3] Besides, within this purported realm of universal disintegration are small havens — crystals, viruses, life, consciousness — local, temporary repeals of the second law, the meaning of which we have yet to assess. Extrapolating from our own, human experience, we know that the long-term effects of consciousness, at least, are liable to be curious.

Thermodynamics and the steam engine: seldom does history offer so neat an illustration of the interactions between economics, technique and pure science. A clear line connects sixteenth century deforestation to some of our deepest insights into the evolution of the universe. The thread is not causal — at least not in any simple sense — it is simply *there*, make of it what you will — an illustration, perhaps, of the strange workings of our chaotic social/intellectual systems.

The science of the nineteenth century, like its economy and society, is marked by rapid, revolutionary change, luxuriant detail and growing specialization. In earlier centuries men like Roger Bacon, Galileo or even Newton could cover most or all of science; philosopher-scientists like Descartes or Leibniz could still dream of creating world-systems encompassing all knowledge. By the end of the eighteenth century, no scientist could make such claims. And it seems unlikely that any historian will ever master the full picture of nineteenth century science — there is simply too much of it, too many special fields, too much detail. But there are landmarks — ideas and individuals whose importance tower above the rest.

As ever, astronomy remained a pre-eminent discipline. By the turn of the century, aided by better telescopes, humanity had lifted its eyes to the vast spaces beyond the stars — the world of the galaxies. The Herschels in England and Messier in France described and catalogued the recently discovered 'island universes'. Their distances remained unknown but, clearly, they were far outside our star systems: the universe was a much more prodigious place than had been thought. Towards the middle of the century Lord Rosse in Ireland built the first really large telescope (a 183 cm reflector) and discovered the spiral structure of many galaxies . . .

Since the advent of Newtonian mechanics, mathematics and deduction had also played a vital role in astronomy. Thus the planet Neptune was discovered through independent predictions by Adams in Britain (1845) and Leverrier in France (1846). Starting with the observed anomalies of Uranus' orbit, after long and difficult calculations they predicted the existence of a new planet — and told astronomers where and when to look. Sir George Airy, the Astronomer Royal, called this example of the deductive powers of theory *sublime*; this it was — as well as a singular triumph for Newtonian mechanics. It was marred, alas, by an acrimonious fight over priorities. The French, in particular, made jingoistic assertions concerning Adams' quite legitimate claims of priority (his prediction, ignored at first by established British astronomers — including the Astronomer Royal — had preceded Leverrier's by a year).[4][*][1] But the known solar system acquired an eighth major planet, eighteen times more massive than the Earth, and thirty times more distant from the sun.

Minor planetary bodies were also studied — like Ceres, which had been observed at the start of the century and analyzed by Gauss. Interestingly, it was discovered shortly after Hegel had averred, on strictly philosophical grounds, that astronomers were wasting their time looking for new planets because, obviously, there could be no more than seven[5] — causing one unhappy historian — W. Durant — to exclaim that 'There is nothing so foolish but it can be found in the philosophers'. This is unfair to philosophy, but perhaps not to Hegel.

Another nineteenth century landmark was the development of electromagnetic theory. After centuries of observation and inconclusive theorizing, electricity and magnetism finally came to be seen as different manifestations of one and the same thing. This was a revolution: it brought to light a whole, new, non-Newtonian domain of physics. And it changed the face of the Earth.

A critical date was 1799: this was when Alessandro Volta put together the first, crude battery — an invention for which he has been honoured by having the basic unit of electrical potential named the *volt*. It allowed serious, systematic experimentation on electric currents to begin. Twenty years later, according to legend, the Dane Oersted (1757-1851), through an accident at a lecture table, showed that a current deflected a compass needle (1820) — it generated a magnetic force. This result was taken up and refined by Henry (1799-1878) in America, Ampère (1775-1836) in France, Gauss (1777-1855) and Ohm (1787-1854) in Germany (all have electric or magnetic units named after them). Ampère, in particular, showed how to calculate the magnetic forces due to a current, as well as those exerted by current-carrying wires on each other. But

---

* Comments James Newman (*loc. cit*): 'The affair was marked by episodes of confusion and fecklessness, of donnish hairpulling and Gallic backbiting and general academic blight.'

the greatest of the nineteenth century experimenters in this field was Michael Faraday (1791-1867).

Faraday, son of a Yorkshire blacksmith, was a self-taught, single-minded, modest and deeply religious man. James Clerk Maxwell eulogized him in these terms:[6]

> It is to be hoped that the nobleness of his simple, undramatic life, will live as long in men's memories as the discoveries which have immortalized his name. Here was no hunger after popular applause, no jealousy of other men's work, no swerving from the well-beloved, self-imposed task of 'working, finishing, publishing'.

Noting the patterns assumed by iron filings near a magnet, Faraday concluded that they gave a picture of the actual direction of the forces acting upon them — the lines of force. He had the brilliant notion that the forces were distributed this way through all of space. This intuition was the basis of the idea of force *field* and of the whole field concept, so central to modern physics. Faraday saw the lines of magnetic force as real perturbations of the space itself — a *state* of an all-pervasive medium or *aether*.

The aether concept had been suggested, in one form or another, by the natural philosophers of other centuries — one remembers Jean de Jandun's explanations of the 'species magnetica' (cf. Chapter 7) or, more recently, Descartes' 'plenum'. Nevertheless, it was a bold step, for it went against the grain of sovereign Newtonian philosophy, for which action-at-a-distance (between magnets, electric charges, planets) was still the final word — a concept believed to be sufficient unto itself.

Faraday's insights and experimental feats were many, and most, like his electrolytic studies, had to do with electrical or magnetic phenomena. But perhaps his greatest achievement was the discovery of induction — the converse of Oersted's effect. The Dane had shown that currents — moving electrical charges — generate magnetic fields. It seemed plausible, if only on grounds of symmetry, that moving or changing magnetic fields should, conversely, generate electric currents. Faraday was so certain of this that he doggedly pursued the problem for seven years. In August 1831, his perseverance and intuition paid off. By opening or closing a switch leading to a primary coil he created a rapidly changing magnetic field (Oersted's phenomenon); this *induced* an electric current in another (secondary) coil which, feeding through a loop of copper wire again produced a magnetic field which deflected a compass needle. Each time he opened and closed the switch, the needle trembled. This was *induction*, the principle of the dynamo and the dawn of a new age for science, technology and society.

Faraday's and Oersted's discoveries are the experimental basis of electromagnetic theory. The corresponding laws can be written in various ways; they relate the rate of variation in time of the electric field to the rate of change in space of the magnetic field (Faraday's law) or, conversely, the variation in time of the magnetic field to the space changes of the electric field (Ampère's law). They give the connection between electricity and magnetism. James Clerk Maxwell (1831-79) was to unify these laws and create *electromagnetic theory*.[6]

The only child of an old Scottish family of landed gentry, Maxwell was carefully educated — at the Edinburgh Academy, the Universities of Edinburgh and Cambridge. He held professorships in natural philosophy, astronomy and physics in Aberdeen, London (King's College) and, after 1871, at Cambridge where he founded the Cavendish Laboratory; he died there in 1879, while still a young man, at the peak of his powers.

For many years, Maxwell's work on electromagnetism was seen as esoteric and difficult; even in 1900, while learning physics at the Zurich Polytechnic, young Einstein had to study Maxwell's equations on his own — almost forty years after their publication, they were still outside the curriculum. During his lifetime, Maxwell's work was appreciated only by a small, international élite. Since he was also a quiet, reserved man who shunned the limelight, he never became as famous as some of his perhaps less remarkable contemporaries or friends. Today, still, most people outside the scientific profession have not heard of him. Yet his work provided the scientific foundation for most of our electrical and magnetic technology, for radar, radio and television, led Einstein to his profound work on relativity, and has inspired modern generations of theoretical physicists. To the public at large, he is the least known of the great all-time geniuses in the history of science.

Both mathematician and experimentalist, Maxwell, like Newton before and Einstein after him, tended to see things
intuitively, in broad, physical analogies. Starting with Faraday's and Ampère's laws, he completed the picture by introducing new concepts and combining these into a simple, lucid
mathematical statement known as *Maxwell's equations*. First published in 1865 in a famous paper entitled 'The Dynamical Theory
of Electromagnetism' they are, said P.G. Tait in his Brittanica
article,

> One of the most splendid monuments ever raised by the genius
> of a single individual.

Feynman, one of our own century's great men, has said that,
in the far future

> the most significant event of the nineteenth century will be
> judged as Maxwell's discovery of the laws of electro-dynamics.
> The American Civil War will pale into provincial insignificance
> in comparison with this important scientific event of the same
> decade.[7]

Today, more than a hundred years later, Maxwell's equations
are still the backbone of our knowledge of electricity and
magnetism. They show how electric and magnetic fields are
interchangeable, how they depend on the point of view of the
observer; motion with respect to an electric field may turn it
into a magnetic one — or *vice-versa* as in the dynamo. Electric
and magnetic fields are *relative*. What Maxwell created was
far more than a mathematical restatement of Ampère's and
Faraday's discoveries — it was a whole new, original outlook on electromagnetism. Maxwell added to the theory an
extra term which had, as yet, no experimental confirmation
but was necessary, he thought, to preserve the symmetry of
his formulation. This term, the so-called *displacement current*,
is an imprint of Maxwell's unique physical intuition upon the
theory. It gave Maxwell's equations their perfection, made
them the basis for the wave theory of light and gave them
the symmetry to sustain, ultimately, Einstein's special theory of relativity. Ludwig Boltzmann (1844-1906), pondering the
beauty and universality of Maxwell's equations, was led to

quote Faust's exclamation at seeing the sign of the cosmos: 'Was it a God who wrote these lines . . .' *These lines* stand close to the very core of our understanding of the universe.

Maxwell had in fact brought about a major *scientific revolution*. Eighteenth and early nineteenth century science saw the world as Newtonian, a world of particles acting upon each other through a universal void, according to definite laws of force-at-a-distance — by what Koestler once called a kind of grappling of ghostly fingers. Maxwell made us see things in terms of fields — in a space no longer a void, not a real emptiness, but something that could be strained and made to change its state by electric charges or magnetic poles or force fields. None of this is, strictly speaking, understandable in ordinary, sensory terms — neither the physicist nor the lay-person can picture the properties of this space or the stresses and strains that it carries. It is an abstract world, beyond the ken of our senses, for which we have no language other than mathematics. Maxwell's contemporaries were mechanical-minded men and women, and they looked for mechanical explanations: they showed little enthusiasm for changing to a viewpoint which transcended mechanics. Even colleagues and friends — all people who admired his work and knew him as a great man — never fully accepted the message. Thus William Thomson (Lord Kelvin), professor of natural philosophy at Glasgow University, whose earlier work had inspired Maxwell, referred to the theory as 'a curious and ingenious, but not wholly tenable hypothesis'. In 1904 he added for good measure that 'the so-called electromagnetic theory of light has not helped us hitherto', — a surprising statement, seeing that the theory not only explained the propagation and properties of light better than earlier ones, but also predicted a whole new spectrum of electromagnetic radiation, the existence of which had already been verified by Hertz (1888) and patented by Marconi (1896).

Nineteenth century science experienced many revolutions; it was an age of scientific giants. To establish among them any kind of hierarchy would be absurd. Maxwell, though, was certainly one of the greatest. Another was Gauss.

Karl Friederich Gauss (1777-1855) has been called, deservedly, the prince of mathematicians. Much of his work was devoted to pure mathematics, of which he founded several

new branches; a lot of it, though, was applied to scientific problems, making him also what we now call an *applied
mathematician*.

Of his many contributions to science, one was of special
philosophical interest. It concerned errors of measurement
and shed light on the problem of scientific certainty. We take
it for granted, today, that all observations have limited accuracy: no measurement is free of error. There are many reasons
for this, most of them uncontrollable and unpredictable. Any
scientist or student who has made measurements near the
limits of an instrument's precision discovers that answers
vary from one try to the next. He or she is then faced with
this dilemma: given a scatter of figures, how does one determine the most likely value, and what does it mean? How, for
instance, does the astronomer find the most probable position
of a star, after taking many readings with a telescope, all of
them slightly different? The problem is the same if you spend
time throwing darts: you are never sure of hitting the bullseye
but, if you are careful, the hits form a *cluster* around the target,
the density of which decreases away from the centre; the latter
is, roughly, the bullseye. The astronomer is simply trying for a
kind of optical bullseye on the star. The best anyone can expect
of measurements is this kind of scatter about a central value.
Gauss showed how to predict the density of these scattered
measurements — how to calculate the probable errors. From
simple mathematical considerations he extracted a universal
curve which allows one to do this and to obtain the most probable value of the quantity being measured — the best guess for
the position of a star.

This underlined a crucial fact: one *never* knows the precise
value of *any* quantity in nature — the best one can do is to
make as many observations as possible and take some sort of
average or, conversely, predict a probable range of values.
The concept of a scientifically deterministic world, in other
words, is nonsense in this respect at least: all predictions use
calculations based upon observations of certain quantities, or
variables; these are *all* to some degree inexact — so then are
the resulting predictions. Sometimes, as in short-term forecasts for simple systems, the results are good enough for
practical purposes; nevertheless, they are not exact. And in

long-term predictions, small initial inaccuracies will grow and may lead to completely wrong answers: predictions into an *indefinite* future are not possible. For a number of reasons, latter-day science takes this as axiomatic; nineteenth century science never quite accepted it. It was felt that, at the very least, ever-improving techniques of measurement would lead to ever smaller errors and to more accurate predictions — one could, with time and diligence, work one's way around the error problem. Scientific and technical progress was seen as a continuously improving process, allowing one to converge indefinitely close to certainty and truth. In this sense, one is justified in calling this century an *age of certainty*. These certitudes were reinforced by the flowering of chemistry, the predictability of chemical reactions and confirmation of the existence of atoms.

Atomic theory had been launched near the turn of the century by three men: a German, Richter (1762-1807), a Frenchman, Proust (1755-1826) and an English Quaker, John Dalton (1766-1844), who showed that specific numbers of atoms combine to form specific molecules — i.e., they combine in definite proportions, which provide a measure of their relative atomic weights. Ancient Greek speculation was thus put on a firm footing and modern atomic chemistry and physics adumbrated at one stroke.

In Dalton's day only some two dozen elements were known; one of chemistry's tasks during the next hundred years would be to bring the number to ninety-three. By the 1860s ,sixty-three elements had been discovered, their properties catalogued, their affinities and combinations understood. Chemistry was ripe for a systematic theory. The framework for this was to be given by *Mendeleyev* (1834-1907).

Dmitri Ivanovitch Mendeleyev was born in Siberia of pioneer stock, the last of a family of fourteen children. He learnt science from an exiled revolutionary — a Decembrist — who married his sister. His Siberian origins, combined with Tsarist red tape, prevented his admission to the University of Moscow. His mother then moved to St Petersburg and secured his admission to the Pedagogical Institute, where he specialized in mathematics, physics and chemistry. Hard and diligent work almost killed him; he contracted tuberculosis around the time of his mother's death and had to take a teaching post in the Crimea to regain his health. Then came formative years in Europe — in Paris and Heidelberg, where he learnt the use of the spectroscope from Kirchhoff. Returning to Russia, he married, published a five-hundred page textbook on organic chemistry and a thesis on alcohol and, at the age of thirty-two, became professor at the University of St Petersburg. This was one of the rare accolades bestowed upon him by official Russia: the Russian establishment always regarded him with suspicion; his views were too progressive, as were his friends — such as his student, the famed anarchist Prince Kropotkin, and his idol Leo Tolstoy. Even after his reputation had become international, after he had been showered with honours abroad, the St Petersburg Academy refused, in 1880, to elect him a member. Sir William Ramsay, the British chemist and co-discoverer with Rayleigh of the rare gas argon, met Mendeleyev at a dinner in London in 1884 and described him as[8]

> . . . a peculiar foreigner every hair of whose head acted in independence of every other . . . He is a nice sort of fellow, but his German is not perfect . . . I suppose he is a Kalmuck or one of those outlandish creatures.

Dmitri Ivanovitch, clearly, was not the establishment type. He died of pneumonia, listening to a reading of Jules Verne's *Journey to the North Pole*.

The work for which Mendeleyev is famous, his classification of the elements — to be known as the *periodic table* (1869) — had in fact been foreshadowed in England (Newlands, 1864) and in Germany (Meyer, 1869). Newlands noticed that, as one went up the scale of atomic weights, every eighth element had similar properties. He called this the law of octaves but was not taken seriously. Meyer, on the other hand, came to detailed conclusions similar to Mendeleyev's but published his results several months later: he deserves, and sometimes gets, a share of the credit. Yet the periodic table is more than a systematic description of periodicities. Mendeleyev saw that it embodied a law — actually a series of deep-seated laws governing the atom, laws it would take physicists half a century to unravel. Any discrepancy had to be explained. And so, when confronted with atomic masses which did not fall in line, he confidently pronounced their measurement to have been in error. Noting unoccupied spaces he stated that new, still undiscovered elements would be found to fill them, and predicted their physical and chemical properties. As the years went by, he was proved right on all counts — as beautiful an example of the uses of induction as any in the history of science. But it is worth noting that this induction process was not Baconian (cf. Chapter 3) — both Mendeleyev and Mayer were guided by previous classification efforts *and* by their knowledge of chemistry.

The nineteenth century was the heroic age of chemistry. Most of the elements making up our world were discovered, isolated and had their properties described. Analytical methods were perfected. Minerals were analyzed — chemical mineralogy and geochemistry were born. So was *organic chemistry* — the study of the substance of living things, the chemistry of life. It began with the synthesis of ethyl alcohol by Hennell (1826) and of urea by Friederich Wohler (1828). This had repercussions well beyond the confines of chemistry: it was a blow against the vitalists who had always believed that organic substances were endowed with a mysterious vital principle, and could only be generated by living things.[1,2]

Following these early syntheses, organic chemistry grew spectacularly: witness Mendeleyev's already mentioned five-hundred page textbook, written in the early 1860s. A great forward step in understanding the chemistry of life was the discovery of the ring structure of benzene in 1865 by the German Kekulé (1829-96). The manner of his insight was curious — and often quoted as a classic instance of the role of unconscious processes. Having wrestled with the problem for a long time, one day Kekulé found himself, as usual, worrying about it; patterns of atoms kept forming and reforming before his eyes, refusing to come to rest. Finally he dozed off and had a dream: he saw a snake swallowing its tail. This was the cue he needed: the molecule of benzene was based on a *closed* ring structure of carbon and hydrogen atoms.

In 1869, far ahead of his times, Friederich Miescher discovered nucleic acids; it would take seventy-five years before their importance to biology, and to the biochemistry of genetics and heredity, would be understood.[2]

Curiously, at the same time, the universal laws of heredity were themselves brought to light — to be ignored, also, until after their discoverer's death. Gregor Mendel (1822-84), an Augustinian monk who had joined the order to pursue a quiet life of study, spent eleven years (1857-68) patiently experimenting with peas in a plot of monastery garden. He showed that the characteristics of living forms must be transmitted by discrete particles — which we now call genes and which we know to be parts of nucleic acid molecules. For each trait offspring receive a gene from each parent; one gene always takes the upper hand: this we call *dominant*; the other is *recessive*. Ordinary arithmetic demonstrates that, in a hybrid population, one out of four will show the recessive trait, three the dominant. In crossing peas, Mendel established that length is dominant over shortness and verified these simple arithmetical laws. Long plants are dominant over short; for people, brown eyes are dominant over blue; amongst Hapsburgs, the long lower lip is dominant. Mendel's paper on the subject, published in the 1866 Brno (Brunn) Society for the Study of Natural Science, was to lie forgotten for thirty-four years (this was in part due to his promotion to abbot and consequent abandonment of his work).

By mid-century, the life sciences were prospering; and all, from medicine and physiology (Pasteur, Koch, Claude Bernard, Pavlov) to palaeontology and zoology (Darwin, Wallace) were finding themselves in conflict with long-held beliefs on the nature of disease, of life and of humanity itself. The greatest controversies swirled around geological, palaeontological and biological evidence which explicitly contradicted traditional religious views on Genesis. The ensuing debates, centring largely on the figure of Charles Darwin, led to what may have been humanity's most radical reappraisal of itself and its place in the world. One must, I think, amend Feynman's statement quoted on page 201, by adding the *theory of evolution* to Maxwell's discovery as another of *two* most important historical events of the nineteenth century.

Hutton's *principle of uniformitarianism* (1785) had postulated, and to some degree demonstrated that, to explain the historical record of ancient rock strata, there was no need to invoke other than existing laws of nature or currently observed processes. Charles Lyell's (1797-1875) *The Principles of Geology: being an Attempt to Explain the Former Changes of the Earth's Surface by reference to Causes now in Operation* (1830-33) firmly established the validity of this principle. Yet, while it insisted on the importance of change and flux in shaping the Earth ('evolutionary geology'), it did not endorse the mutability of species (biological evolution). Lyell's view was that evolution could not be accepted unless a valid mechanism be given. In terms of early nineteenth century thinking, evolutionary geology was revolutionary enough — contradicting, among others, such authorities as Cuvier (1769-1831) who propounded the view that geologic history consisted of a sequence of catastrophes separating sharp faunal changes (God's hand was at work here — varied species were being replaced by divine intervention).

'The great merit of *The Principles*,' said Darwin, 'was that it altered the whole tone of one's mind.' His mentor, the Revd Henslow, upon giving Darwin a copy for his journey on the Beagle, admonished him 'not to pay any attention to it except in regards to facts, for it is altogether wild as far as theory goes.' Yet nineteenth-century geologists accepted the good sense behind Hutton's and Lyell's uniformitarianism. However, to use the idea that currently operating forces are also those that shaped the Earth in its past, one must understand what these forces are — which nineteenth-century physicists and geologists did not (*could* not, in fact). As a result the earth sciences remained embroiled in internal disagreements between various theories — essentially until modern times . . .

Darwin accepted the philosophical outlook of uniformitarianism; but his interest lay in the processes that had produced the incredible profusion of life forms he saw everywhere around him. And, while the mechanism eluded him for years, everything pointed to *evolution*. The idea as such was not new: Buffon (1707-88) had already accepted the possibility of 'transformism' — albeit only in exceptional cases, and Haekel and Lamarck had been out and out evolutionists.[9]* But in Britain the social climate did not encourage frontal attacks on the biblical story of Genesis. Some staunchly maintained that fossils were artefacts planted by God, or perhaps the Devil, to test our faith; to give up belief in one's divine origins is not easy.

Charles Darwin and Alfred Russel Wallace introduced the concept of biological evolution due to natural selection. Not all their arguments are accepted today; there are still controversies concerning the mechanics of the process; however, the basic concept of evolution through natural selection is no longer in doubt. It is a law of the universe we live in — which, like the equations of physics or chemistry, is expected to hold true in any corner of the cosmos in which there is life.

Darwin and Wallace are curious characters in the history of science. In modern terms neither had the credentials to call himself a scientist. They were *naturalists* — a species which, for a time, seemed in danger of extinction. Both started as amateurs with a strong interest in plants, beetles and the like. Of the two, Darwin had the better education, the broader view, and was, perhaps, the better writer. He offered the most detailed and thorough statement; which is perhaps why he is the more celebrated.

Charles Darwin was born on 12th February 1809, on the same day as Abraham Lincoln. His father, a successful physician, was well off; his grandfather Erasmus Darwin, a poet and botanist, had made a brave, speculative attempt to show that all life descended from a single, original filament: evolutionary ideas and the questioning of established beliefs were no novelty in the family. Destined first for the profession of medicine, then for the clergy, Charles' academic record was undistinguished. His view was that the seven years spent at Butler's school were

* Lamarck's views, and the role of acquired characteristics in his theory, have been, and still are, endlessly debated. A lucid introduction to this, and to the nineteenth century evolution debates, will be found the Open University volume The Crisis of Evolution, (J.H. Brooke); these problems are intimately intertwined with theology and beliefs.

'simply a blank' and his time at Cambridge 'wasted, as far as academic studies were concerned'. However, he enjoyed collecting beetles and went for walks with the botany professor, the Revd John S. Henslow.

It was Henslow who, recognizing Darwin's gift for observation, recommended him for the (unsalaried) 'situation' of naturalist aboard the *HMS Beagle*, outward bound on a scientific circumnavigation of the Earth. After some deliberation — which included securing his father's reluctant consent — Darwin accepted. 'The time,' he said, 'I do not think anyhow would be more thrown away than if I stayed at home.' So he went to meet Captain Fitzroy, who commanded the *Beagle*, and almost did not get the 'situation' because the man thought poorly of his nose (he felt it indicated insufficient determination to stand up to the rigours of the sea). Darwin, indeed, was desperately sick through much of the voyage, but displayed plenty of determination. For five years, from December 1831 till October 1836, the *Beagle* wound its slow course up and down the coasts of South America, through the Galapagos, Tahiti, Australia . . . Everywhere Darwin observed, marvelled at the variety of species and, though he did not yet use the word, at the delicacy of their adaptation. He filled his notebook, wrote letters, read *Paradise Lost* and Lyell's *Principles*, and pondered Nature's profusion of species; he never doubted the reality of evolution, but the mechanism eluded him. He quarrelled with Fitzroy, a conservative who believed in the literal truth of the story of Genesis. To Darwin's credit, they remained on amicable terms through most of the trip. Nevertheless, he complained later that 'The difficulty of living on good terms with a Captain of a Man-of-War is much increased by its being almost mutinous to answer him as one would anyone else.'[10]

After his return to England, Darwin married his cousin, Emma Wedgewood (1839). In 1842 they moved to Downe, which was to be Darwin's home for the rest of his life. After 1841 his health was poor — he either contracted some tropical disease during his voyage or, more likely, was being slowly poisoned by a prescribed medication containing arsenic. For the rest of his life, he had to marshal his time carefully — working only during the few hours of the day when he felt fit. Nevertheless, his output of books, papers, notes and articles was huge. In 1836 he had returned with a vast store of observations that did not fit existing theories. He did not yet see the answer to what he called 'The mystery of mysteries': how had the incredible variety of living things come about? Clearly, they had diverged from common stock. But how?

It is usually difficult to determine the seminal influence — the stimulus which triggers the creative mind. In Darwin's case, however, we have his own account: it was a chance reading, in 1838, of Malthus' 1798 *Essay on the Principle of Population*, a work popular with early nineteenth century radical philosophers. Parson Thomas Malthus had pointed out that population, inevitably, increases faster than the food supply; this led to a stimulus for self-improvement. Said the good parson:

> Had population and food increased in the same ratio, it is probable that man might never have emerged from the savage state.

Such simple observations had, unfortunately, the makings of extremely callous social attitudes. Proponents of nineteenth-century *laissez-faire* — which forced abandonment of Pitt's bill for poor relief to large families, and allowed millions to starve in the Irish potato famine — merely appealed to Malthus to wash their hands of responsibility. Engels was to see Malthus' ideas as 'the most open declaration of war of the bourgeoisies upon the proleteriat'. However, what critics have tended to ignore was that, as is so often the case, the trouble lay not in Malthus' arithmetic, which was unexceptionable, but in the conclusions people drew from it — there are, after all, sensible and humane ways of controlling population; but they require effort and some level of sacrifice on the part of all elements of society.

Darwin, on the other hand, understood the logic of Malthus' proposition — he quickly saw the fact that population increases faster than the food supply as a universal ecological regulator, resulting in savage competition. Here, then, was a sensible mechanism: animal species *must* compete to survive; the inadequate are killed off and the survivors, better fitted for their environment, live on to breed. Nature, in effect, selects forms which are well adapted, eliminates those that are not. Such new forms — mutations — arise by chance; the inadequate ones, by definition, disappear. In his autobiography Darwin recorded his enthusiasm at this revelation:

> Under these circumstances favourable variations tend to be preserved, and unfavourable ones destroyed. The result of this would be the formation of a new species. Here, then, I had a theory by which to work.

This was Malthus' doctrine of human population, writ large to include all forms of environmental pressure, and extended to all living forms, to all life on Earth.

Others, including some of Darwin's contemporaries, had held similar ideas; but *they* had been speculating; Darwin had a vast collection of *facts* to support his theory. In no hurry to publish, only in 1844 did he compose a two hundred and thirty-page manuscript, which he proceeded to put away with money and instructions for his wife to publish, in case of death. Darwin, it seems, would have liked to die in peace before his theory was made public. He may have known the storm it would raise, and would rather it blew in his absence.

By June 1858, Darwin had completed half of an expanded treatise on evolution. He then received a manuscript by A.R. Wallace, who had written to him from the Moluccas for an opinion. Wallace also suggested that the manuscript be forwarded to Lyell. Darwin was startled to find in it a complete summary of his own theory; a painful problem of priorities had arisen. He forwarded the manuscript to Lyell and to his friend Sir Joseph Hooker and put himself in their hands. They sent Wallace's essay to the Linnaean society together with an abstract of Darwin's work, with an explanatory note to the secretary of the society. both were read to a meeting of the society on 1st July 1858; Darwin's paper was given first and created hardly a stir. But Darwin's great opus, *On the Origin of Species*, appeared on 14th November 1859, and was instantly sold out. It would alter forever the way humanity saw itself and its fellow creatures.

Alfred Russel Wallace (1823-1913), like Darwin, began as an amateur naturalist. At the age of twenty-five, after an indifferent education and a start as a surveyor, he took up collecting specimens in distant lands, selling them to museums and collectors. Having no private means, his path was thornier than Darwin's. After four years on the Amazon, he lost his entire collection in a shipwreck. But, like Darwin, he was tenacious; and, like him, he was an acute observer, had marvelled at Nature's diversity and had puzzled long and hard over the differentiation of species. He too read Malthus and had the same vision strike him, in 1858, twenty years later.

It is, I think, to both men's credit that they willingly shared the honours for their idea — one of the most important insights in the history of thought.

Evolutionary ideas had been around for a long time — at least since Anaximander, 2,500 years ago; more recently Lamarck had propounded evolution in terms of adaptation and transmission of acquired characteristics and Darwin, probably, was indebted to him. But Darwin offered a mechanism: *chance* variations (mutations) were the key, and these survived to give new species *if* they were adaptive. A major difference between him and his forerunners, also, was that he produced a powerful mass of evidence to support his theory. There were many difficulties in his thesis — inconsistencies and gaps — and not a few Darwinian tenets on 'survival of the fittest' (as Herbert Spencer, not Darwin, called it) have, by now, been extensively qualified and some have been rejected. But the basic paradigm was correct.[10]

The *Origin of Species*, as Darwin may have foreseen, excited a monumental controversy. As at least one perceptive writer[9] has pointed out, the public had, heretofore, had its own image of the scientist; but here was a scientist advancing an image of the public — and what an image! Our ancestor had been a species of ape — decently extinct and no longer capable of embarassing us, yet still an ape. It is doubtful that we can recapture today the sense of outrage that assailed most good, middle-class Victorians at this bit of news. Abuse and sarcasm were heaped on Darwin from all directions. The clergy were, of course, among Darwin's most vehement critics. Yet many enlightened theologians sided with him. As Charles Kingsley put it[9]

> We know of old that God was so wise that he could make all things; but, behold, he is so much wiser than even that, that he can make all things make themselves.

At the same time, some who supported natural selection would — as with Malthus' ideas — draw their own oversimplified conclusions — from Karl Marx who claimed that Darwin's book had provided him with a scientific basis for class warfare, to the Revd Josiah Strong's blatant white supremacist creed which spoke of the 'final competition of races for which the Anglo-Saxon is being schooled'.[9]*

Physicists, led by William Thomson (Lord Kelvin) were largely against Darwin. Their chief argument was that calculations of the cooling of the Earth would not countenance the vast time spans demanded by the theory of evolution. Kelvin allowed at most 40 million years for the age of the Earth. Darwin knew he needed far more:

> I am greatly troubled at the short duration of the world according to Sir William Thomson for I require for theoretical views a very long period before the Cambrian formation.

In 1873 Kelvin announced: 'We find at every turn something to show the utter futility of (Darwin's) philosophy' — a fine sample of a powerful, authoritative and quite fallacious statement issuing from incomplete data. The discovery of radioactivity by Becquerel (1896) and Rutherford's observation that it was accompanied by heat (1904) would give a mechanism for keeping the Earth warm through the eons; it was even to offer, soon after, an accurate means of dating ancient life forms and rocks. And so, after Darwin's death in 1882, the time-scale argument was settled, permanently, in his favour. The question troubled him till his dying day; but, as the voyage of the Beagle had already proved, he was a determined man: he stuck to his guns. In his old age, the worst of the storm was over; he died honoured and revered at the age of seventy-three. Only Wallace, who outlived him by twenty-five years, witnessed the final triumph of natural selection over the

---

* Today's Social Darwinists and Sociobiologists are, it seems, carrying on analogous traditions.

arguments of 'the physicists'.

The nineteenth century was a period of prodigious scientific advances, during which whole new fields of science arose. Some, like thermodynamics, prospered quickly; others, like evolution, bred storms of controversy before being accepted and some, like Mendel's genetics, were born a generation before their time. It is not possible to pick *one* field and say: this characterizes the period, this was the century's greatest scientific advance. Nevertheless, three achievements stand out: the birth of thermodynamics, Maxwell's unification of electricity and magnetism, and the Darwin-Wallace theory of evolution through natural selection. These may well be seen, someday, as the most important historical events of the nineteenth century.

Technological growth was also spectacular — perhaps more so than science, in the public mind. Transport, electrification, chemical industries, the control of disease — the list is endless — were altering society in deep and irreversible ways.

By 1900 technology's power was beyond anything other centuries had dreamt of. History had no precedent for this; and humanity was not prepared. The industrial revolution created huge difficulties — pollution, slums, savage exploitation of labour, social and political turmoil. Engineers, entrepreneurs and some social philosophers felt that these problems would be solved by the same methods that had produced them; awed by the accomplishments of science, they saw therein a lesson to be applied. This sustained a curious optimism, a faith which said, in effect, that we were on the right path — a little more effort, a little goodwill, and our newly acquired scientific-technological muscle, *the power of knowledge*, would solve all problems and lead us on to fresh, utopian worlds. Marxism, for instance, proposed to do what Francis Bacon had preached — apply the methods of science to the solution of all our social and economic woes. The real complexities had yet to be gauged; running through this kind of thinking were major, unspoken assumptions. One was the existence of a method — *the scientific method* — lurking behind this explosion of technological power. Another was, quite simply, that, barring such minor unpleasantness as human perversity and errors of measurement or judgment, the world was intrinsical-ly *predictable* — infinitely predictable, if one went along with Laplace.

We know today that these assumptions were wrong. Two monstrous world wars, massive unemployment, Third World poverty and starvation, proliferating totalitarianism, have cruel-ly demonstrated that the nineteenth century idols were flawed, its faith too simple. Yet it is all too easy, with the knowledge of hindsight, to smile condescendingly at past generations; we have, most likely, inherited much of their blindness and their arrogance. Future generations may find us equally naive or uncouth. So, if smile we must, let us do so with understanding, gently.

CHAPTER TWELVE

The Postmodern World

Twenty-one years after the end of the First World War on 1st September 1939 the German armies invaded Poland and a curtain of madness fell again upon the world. For twenty years the clouds had been gathering — ever since the blunders of Versailles and the consequent, all but predictable rise of Nazism. Spreading like vermin through Europe, it seemed, for a few years, as if fascism would conquer everything in its path.

The Second World War was, in almost every way, even more savage than the first. The dead will never be counted: there were probably more than fifty millions, mostly noncombatants, systematically slaughtered by German, Russian and Allied military forces. The Nazis, in particular, set new standards of horror in the hell-holes of Auschwitz, Buchenwald, Dachau, Treblinka . . .

To put a stop to this nightmare took more than five years, millions of lives and unimaginable suffering. The war ended in the Pacific with the great fireballs of Hiroshima and Nagasaki — history's crowning monument to the amorality of power and the perversion of knowledge. In Hiroshima alone 66,000 people were killed outright by one *small* fission weapon; thousands more exposed to the bomb's lethal flash died and are still dying of radiation-induced cancers.

After the monstrous mushroom clouds had cleared, after the bomb's radioactive corruption had settled and the victims counted, it was said, and said rightly, that science had lost its innocence. The utility of science for the killing industry had, of course, long been understood — since Archimedes, at least. But the Second World War established this with such ultimate brutality that even the dimmest politician would henceforth understand something of the knowledge-power equation — the fact that, given money and intelligent administration, scientists

207

could be organized into teams to milk knowledge for *any* purpose. Thus society and government finally and wholeheartedly
embraced Francis Bacon's dictum — but spurned his caveats.
Hiroshima was the apotheosis of the lesson; death had been the
teacher.

So began science's time of affluence, the era of *Big Science*,
of the great accelerators of CERN, Fermilab and Serpukhov,
of vast radio telescopes, of spaceflight and moon landings.
Many have reflected upon the ironies of scientific progress.
The manner in which wars foster new techology is obvious;
that they be *necessary* for the advancement of *science* is more
doubtful. But the Second World War convinced governments
and public to support science on a previously undreamt-of
scale* — a process at all times and in all ways actively encouraged by the scientific profession. A crooked yet unequivocal
path connects Buchenwald and Auschwitz, Hiroshima and
Nagasaki, to the great insights of modern science; some of
our worst crimes are not unrelated to the proudest creations
of our mind. Why this should be so, whether it be inevitable
or not, I cannot say. But I suspect that the moral cost of this
connection has been great — a factor I try to keep in mind
when reading eulogies of modern science.

In this century, the advances — in all fields of science —
have been massive. The years since the Second World War
have witnessed revolutions in thinking, new insights of great
subtlety and beauty across the whole front of human knowledge. Mathematics, physics, cosmology, astronomy, geology,
biology, chemistry, computer science — these fields, and
many others, have been revolutionized not once but many
times. Writers like Lewis Thomas, Carl Sagan and S.J. Gould,
have communicated some of the poetry, exhilaration and beauty attendant to this knowledge: they have made it possible for us
all to be science addicts, without having to learn the craft — in
much the same way, perhaps, that one need not be a musician
to enjoy Mozart or Bach. Nevertheless, keeping up with the

---

*In the USA, pre-the Second World War yearly government expendi-
ture on 'basic' science was of the order of ten million dollars. After
the war it had soared into the billions — i.e., it jumped by a factor of
a hundred.[1]

generalist 'semi-popular' articles in *Nature, Science* or *Scientific American*, with 'popular' books, the press or the offerings of the media induces a certain helplessness — in this day and age we cannot even begin to have what Thomas Sprat, writing about Francis Bacon, called 'the true Imagination of the whole state of the Enterprise'.

At no other time in history have science and technology impinged so actively upon our lives, produced such dizzying rates of change, or raised so many practical, philosophical or moral questions.

Phenomenal advances in computer design suggest that much of what now passes for thinking will soon be done for us by machines. It is conceivable, for instance, that 'intelligent' machines (artificial intelligence) may one day take over many of the activities we currently describe as science. One can object, quite reasonably it seems, that so-called artificial intelligence is not intelligence at all. But then it could also transpire that much of what we call science may not require real intelligence — merely training and persistence, at which computers manifestly out-perform us. Redundancy may await us all.

J.K. Galbraith* neatly states the case: 'It is a common public impression, not discouraged by scientists, engineers and industrialists, that modern scientific, engineering and industrial achievements are the work of a new and quite remarkable race of men. This is pure vanity; were it so, there would be few such achievements. The real accomplishment of modern science and technology consists in taking ordinary men, informing them narrowly and deeply and then, through appropriate organization, arranging to have their knowledge combined with that of other specialized but equally ordinary men. This dispenses with the need for genius. The resulting performance, though less inspiring, is far more predictable' . . .

Peculiar, too, are the much-touted possibilities of genetic engineering whereby, through detailed knowledge and manipulation of genes, we may acquire God-like powers for changing existing life-forms or creating new ones. The potential benefits to agriculture, stock-breeding or biological pest control are obvious. But things are not going to stop there.

Currently underway in the USA is the multi-billion dollar human genome project, the purpose of which is to map fully our genetic blueprint. There shall be clear medical benefits to such knowledge. But its general availability raises alarming spectres. One recalls, in particular, long-standing speculations by geneticists and molecular biologists concerning the manipulation of our gene structure to create new varieties of humans — better ones, of course, superhuman ones perhaps. But who, one may ask, will design these superbeings? As at least one critic has remarked: can a child design an adult, or a crook an honest person?*

To attempt a popular summary of the whole enterprise for late twentieth century buffs would be a Herculaean task; even if it were possible, the explosive growth of knowledge ensures that it would be superannuated before it was finished — one does not write books on contemporary history in the middle of a revolution.

But, in the onrushing tide of science, two broad sectors are of absorbing interest for all who are concerned with its wider philosophical implications. The first deals primarily with the beginnings and intimate structure of the universe (cosmology and particle physics), the other with the nature, birth and history of life on Earth (biophysics, evolution). These domains of science shed light upon our most ancient riddles: How was the universe created? When? How did life begin? How did *we* evolve? — questions that have haunted Western thinkers since the days of Thales of Miletos, 2,500 years ago, and before. Here too, we are on shifting ground — new knowledge keeps pouring in, the focus changes, theories are modified. Nevertheless, an outline — the beginnings of a consensus — appears to be emerging. For the first time in our history there is enough hard data to allow serious, mature scientific work on these matters. We may not be ready to fulfil Einstein's hopes 'to know how God created this world'; but we are closer than we have ever been: we have at least the makings of a modern myth of Genesis.

One of the great cosmological insights of this century

---

*   Mary Midgeley[3] gives a careful, perceptive discussion of these and other related issues.

occurred when, in 1929, Edwin Hubble showed that the universe is expanding at an enormous rate: the most distant galaxies our telescopes can sense are fleeing from us at speeds approaching that of light.

Going backwards in time and reversing, mentally, this expansion takes us into an odd world: ten or twenty billion years ago, all matter, the whole cosmos with its billions of galaxies and a billion billion suns concentrated in a tiny space — the size of an egg, perhaps, or a pinhead, and exploding outwards at the speed of light. Some prosaic soul called this the *Big Bang*, and the name has stuck.

What initiated this cosmic explosion? How did it all start? Do we *need* a creator? The theorists, resourceful as ever, have come up with some strange answers — models which, for the twentieth century scientific mind, are acquiring a ring of truth. These are the *inflationary universe* models, of which there are several variants, and which bring together concepts from quantum theory and Einstein's general relativity — in ten (or more)-dimensional (*supersymmetric*) spaces. A key idea in quantum theory is that even an ordinary, four-dimensional Euclidean vacuum is not truly empty, but is actually in a constant state of fluctuation: over sufficiently minute time intervals, matter-antimatter particle pairs (for instance, electrons and positrons) appear and disappear at random points in space and time. These vacuum fluctuations, say today's theorists, also take place in a ten-dimensional universe — with the added and important difference that here a fluctuation can be unstable, explode and generate a whole universe. The Big Bang, then, may be but a random fluctuation that became unstable and, so to speak, got out of hand. As someone put it, it was the ultimate free lunch.

The behaviour — the physics — of matter and energy at the inception of our universe is beyond anything we are familiar with in our laboratories. Yet there are places in the universe at which similarly extreme conditions are found: these are the *black holes* — curious objects predicted by the equations of general relativity, remnants of supernovas, resulting from the collapse of particularly massive stars; points in space and time at which infalling matter is disappearing from our universe — and radiating a great deal of energy as it does so. We find them as invisible companions in double star systems, at the centres of galaxies (our own included) and, far out, at the limit of what our instruments can see, near the boundaries of the universe, as *quasars*: oversize black holes, more massive than a billion suns, at the centre of galaxies billions of light years away. We 'see' these on our radio arrays as minute signals from the infalling matter — ghostly whispers of radiation from the very edge of space and time.

The universe is full of odd objects — it is a far bigger, stranger, more violent place than astronomers and physicists of previous generations had ever dreamt of — a world of vast explosions, titanic energy sources, of neutron stars so dense that a thimbleful of their matter has a mass of millions of tons. The world of high-energy physics is, in its own way, equally strange. Interestingly, it too is converging upon the problems of the early universe.

High-energy physics is so named because, in studying the fundamental, smallest building blocks of matter, one uses high-energy particles to bombard other particles. The reason for this is simple. According to quantum theory, a particle may behave like a wave whose wavelength is inversely proportional to the energy: the higher the energy, the shorter the wavelength. On the other hand, the size of the smallest object that is comfortably 'seen' by a wave is of the order of a wavelength. It follows that, the smaller the object we wish to detect, the higher must be the energy of the bombarding 'particles'. And so, ever since E.O. Lawrence built his first small cyclotron in 1930, physicists have built increasingly powerful accelerators. If one were to encapsulate in one sentence the history of experimental particle physics after the Second World War, it would be this: ever greater particle energies have been generated by ever larger accelerators to look at ever smaller bits of matter. Truly, *reality* in physics is rather like an onion: for every layer you peel off, you find another. By the turn of the century, science had established the existence of atoms. Then these were seen to consist of electrons and nuclei. Next, the nuclei were found to be made of neutrons, protons and other particles, such as mesons. Today, the neutrons and protons have themselves been broken down into quarks. Binding these are the so-called *colour force* fields — the quantum theory of which is called, logically enough, quantum chromodynamics or QCD. Various fields are at play, holding together the bits and pieces in the nucleus — with peculiar yet measurable properties to which physicists, in a kind of playful bewilderment, have given names like flavour, colour and strangeness. Whether these successive layers of reality end somewhere — whether there is a bottom line to all this — is uncertain. One thing, however, seems clear: we cannot, in laboratory experiments, go much beyond the current layer — it is a simple matter of economics; the energy requirements are too great.

Present day research is trying to gather all particles and fields under one banner — a single, internally consistent theory which would tell us *why* matter is made of quarks, electrons and so forth, *why* these have the properties we observe, *why* gravity is so much weaker than other force fields and so on. The final goal — the Holy Grail of theoretical physicists — is a fully unified theory, unified in the same sense that Maxwell first wed electric and magnetic forces into one electromagnetic field. In favour here, as in cosmology, are the supersymmetric theories. These state that our universe is at least ten-dimensional, that there are *strings* in this space and — shades of Pythagoras — that their natural modes of vibration define the observed particles. And so it appears that the more enthusiastic theoretical physicists now talk of supersymmetry as if it were to yield, soon, a *Theory of Everything* (TOE). The TOE, it is said, will in fact allow us to deal with the physics of the beginnings of an inflationary universe. Here cosmology and physics will become one, and give us material for our modern picture of Genesis.

When — *if* — this day comes we will truly be entitled to use the four-thousand year-old words of Ahmose the scribe and claim, with some justification, that we have a theory 'for enquiring into nature, and for knowing all that exists, every mystery . . . every secret'. But we are not quite there — we need, at the very least, more data from the subnuclear world. Historically speaking, of course, it has ever been thus; always, we have felt on the verge of unlocking the last secret. Ahmose tells us the ancient Egyptians thought so. The men and women of the Enlightenment were certain that *all* was about to be revealed by the methods of science. In the late nineteenth century physicists like Kelvin assumed they had pretty much done it all. In 1928 Max Born stated publicly that, in six months, physics would be over. In retrospect, such naiveté is seen to be less a reflection of arrogance than a simple failure of the imagination. And so, while I am not a physicist, I am uncomfortable in the face of these claims for a TOE. History, if nothing else, suggests that we remain sceptical. We shall be in good company — the very best: shortly before he died, Richard Feynman also expressed his doubts.[4]

Nevertheless, we are, it seems, catching a glimpse of how our universe began and how it is constructed. If we ever complete it, this will be a breathtaking tale. For the time being we may see it as one half of the modern story of creation, the main substance — and poetry — of which will be found in Stephen Hawking's *A Brief History of Time*.[5]

The other great contemporary myth — the other half of the story — is no less grand, and may have been philosophically more influential. It deals with the story of life on Earth and its principal shaper — *evolution by natural selection*. This is a world view which includes us as players, while reaching down, at the same time, to the molecular level — to genetic blueprints, DNA and RNA molecules and, in a dim geological past, to the first replicators.

The nineteenth century laid the foundations: Darwin and Wallace gave us a credible model of evolution, Mendel gave us genetics, organic chemistry learnt to deal with an increasingly complex collection of compounds. Now, in the second half of the twentieth century, all these strands have been pulled together.

Thus we are beginning to understand *the cell*. Discovered in 1665 by Robert Hooke and Nehemia Grew, it was, for a long time, seen as the simplest unit of life; today, we know it is not — viruses and viroids are simpler. But cells are the units from which *we* are built; the cells of our bodies, prior to specialization, are not so different from the myriad unicellular organisms inhabiting the planet. Indeed, we must see ourselves as symbiotic structures, cooperative ventures between hordes of specialized cells tirelessly, systematically keeping organs working, lungs breathing, the blood flowing and the brain thinking — a giant hive of many trillion units going about their business of maintaining *us*.

Each cell is a complex mechanism, a mass of protoplasm encased in a membrane, surrounding a nucleus, organelles and mitochondria acting as tiny power plants, a miniature chemical factory which breathes, eats, excretes, moves and reproduces — itself a marvellous, delicately balanced symbiotic system of ancient lineage. Replication and reproduction are the keys to its existence — and to ours. And we are beginning to understand the process. The basic plans are in the nucleus, the principle the same for all living forms, be they one-celled like the amoeba, or many-celled like you and I: the nucleus contains the blueprint of the whole organism. This blueprint, or *genome*, is not just a diagram: it is an organizer, an *active* blueprint, an executive entity which ensures that its instructions are obeyed. In ways we still do not understand, it regulates and directs the processes of synthesis and reproduction of all cell material — a miraculously precise and intricate procedure. The blueprint itself is in the form of a nucleic acid: a DNA molecule which, in the chromosomes, is the main carrier of genetic information. This, then, is the key to life: a trillion atoms, chain-like, a giant amongst molecules, and built of a great number of simpler blocks. As Watson, Crick, Wilkins and Franklin showed in 1953, it consists of two strands wound upon themselves as a double helix. Each strand has a backbone of esters and sugars supporting an immensely long sequence of nucleotide bases — relatively simple units, four kinds of them, making up a four-letter alphabet; their sequencing is the message. Here are the instructions, to be interpreted and executed by RNA molecules, which allow the cell to reproduce, the organism to survive: the very substance of life.

Different segments of the DNA molecule — groups of nucleotide bases — regulate the design and growth of the whole, as well as different parts of the organism; these are the genes. They decide the general form (man, woman or mouse) and the details (eye colour, nose shape, etc.,). They are the information carriers predicted by Mendel a hundred years ago. In sexual reproduction two special cell types, the egg and the sperm, each containing but one strand of the parent DNA, combine and fuse these to give a new double-stranded molecule representing a mixture of genetic traits. The result is an almost infinite variety of possible individual types.

During its lifetime, any cell or living creature is subject to endless influences, buffetings by chemical or thermal effects, cosmic rays, natural or artificial radioactivity — all of which may damage a base or gene in the DNA chain, altering the structure of the blueprint and changing the instructions in minor or major ways. Cells or animals which succeed in translating these into living forms are *mutations*, many of which do not survive. A few do, however: here we have the source of the random variations Darwin had postulated — mutations of which only the harmless or beneficial will live to reproduce through the generations. This near-tautology is the essential idea behind *natural selection* — the philosophy, mechanisms and detail of which have generated more argument and controversy than any other scientific insight of the last two centuries. Mendel, Darwin and now molecular biology: it all links up, persuasively and beautifully. The intricacies of life's mechanisms may still elude us, but the overall picture is emerging.

In broad terms, then, we understand the physical and chemical basis of evolution. The details of the family tree may still be vague but we see, more or less, how all life on Earth may have descended from one original, simple form. Our image of this common ancestor is, as yet, vague and speculative. We are certain neither of its precise nature, nor of the manner or time of its arrival. There are, it seems, two main schools of thought.

One has it that, over the eons, the basic building blocks of life arrived from space — on interstellar dust motes, from the great dilute gas clouds scattered through the galaxy, on comets. And organic molecules, both simple and complex, have indeed been detected by astronomers in space, and also in meteorites. Some proponents of this view suggest even that self-replicating molecules, i.e., life itself may have developed in that inimical environment. Reaching Earth, they would have found ideal conditions and, rather like bacteria landing in a Petri dish, multiplied exuberantly — an intriguing, but, one gathers, not a majority view.

More generally accepted is the theory that our original, common ancestor evolved here, on Earth. It is thought that, before life appeared on the planet, there was water — a primeval ocean, perhaps. Floating in it were molecules of various kinds; amongst these were structures built of carbon, hydrogen, nitrogen — methane, formaldehyde, ammonia and the like. Such molecules exist everywhere: in space, on other planets, in meteorites; the basic chemical *desiderata* for life's building blocks are not hard to come by. It all began, by this scenario, in or near an ocean, maybe in shallow water, in drying scum along the beaches or perhaps, as Darwin suggested, in a warm tidal pool at the edge of some long-forgotten sea.

In 1953, already, Stanley Miller had subjected simple mixtures of this sort to ultraviolet light and electric sparks (artificial lightning). After some weeks of this treatment one gets a weak brown broth of more complex molecules — containing, among other things, amino-acids. Some such process occurred, most likely, in or near the primeval ocean, leading to this kind of pre-biotic soup. Given more time and continued irradiation, larger molecules would have formed. In the absence of life, these floated around unmolested. But, wherever the concentration was sufficient, they collided with each other, or with simpler molecules, with amino-acids, with nucleotide bases, jostling a variety of compounds, adding a piece here, losing another there — reacting, endlessly, in random ways. It is hard to guess how long this phase lasted — millions or hundreds of millions of years perhaps, it does not really matter. There was time. And then, one day, a remarkable molecule was formed: a *replicator*.

We do not know the form of this first replicator, but it must have acted as a template. Perhaps like today's DNA or RNA molecules it produced copies of itself, attaching building blocks out of the pre-biotic soup to complementary slots on its own body, then releasing into the environment a copy of itself, perhaps a kind of negative, which repeated the process . . . These early replicators did not have to be efficient, or well-adapted: there was no competition, not at first — they existed in what Carl Sagan has called a kind of molecular Garden of Eden.[6] Under the influence of sunlight, cosmic rays, radioactivity, lightning, or simple chemistry, mutations appeared. Some, more stable than others, tended to live longer, or reproduce more rapidly, or replicate more accurately. These and other, environmental, factors determined which types survived, and in what numbers. Better strains, more error-free, more stable, or more aggressive, prospered. Some adopted offensive, carnivorous strategies — to feed, most likely, on their ancestral species; others developed defensive coatings, walls of protein, *membranes* to fend off their predatory cousins; the first cell-like creatures may have appeared in this way. The battle for survival was on — an unthinking, inevitable, chance-ridden struggle of the replicators for self-perpetuation.

This basic replicator scenario is surely incomplete. Even at its simplest life is not mere replication; living things also use energy, which they extract from the environment — a process known as metabolism. But metabolism and replication are logically separable. One may thus imagine life as arising in *two* separate events: as proteins capable of metabolism (but not replication), and as replicators incapable of metabolism. Freeman Dyson has pointed out that the replicators could have appeared last, and drawn their matter from, i.e., *fed upon*, the proteins. Next, the replicators simplified the process by becoming symbiotic — parasitic to the proteins.[7] These earliest cell-like organisms had no proper nucleus and have therefore been named *prokaryotes*, from the Greek karyos (nut, nucleus), and were far simpler than any modern cell. *Eukaryotes*, built around a proper nucleus housing the genetic information, had to be a later development; but the time scales are unknown.

Some of the Earth's most ancient rocks, in Swaziland, Greenland, Canada, Australia tell us that three billion years ago, already, the age of the simple prokaryotes was over: blue-green algae had made their appearance — and had, one assumes, begun exuding into the atmosphere the oxygen it would need, someday, to support our kind of life. But except for these, some coral-like structures and a Pre-Cambrian bed of soft-bodied fossils in Australia, the record is sparse until the beginning of the Cambrian period, about 570 million years ago. At this point, suddenly, the Earth's ancient seas were teeming with new, surprisingly complex species. To the palaeontologist, this explosion of life forms is something of an enigma. Modern studies show, however, that the arithmetic of natural selection can be full of surprises — especially when so much of the data is missing. It is possible, too, that the contrast with the Pre-Cambrian is due, in large measure, to the emergence of species which manufactured hard protective coatings — exoskeletons like those of the trilobites, or the lime-rich covers of the shellfish. The soft parts of a creature are not easily preserved and, so goes this explanation, most Pre-Cambrian life had soft, unprotected bodies and left few fossils. It is also known that great ice sheets covered much of the planet in the late Pre-Cambrian; there is therefore an alternative theory which says that the change to a warmer climate led to a sudden proliferation of life in the Cambrian. Clearly, a large measure of uncertainty still attends the problem.

Thereafter — for the last 500 million years, just over ten per cent of Earth's history — the story of life is better documented. Of special, chauvinistic interest to us is the evolution of the vertebrates.

All vertebrates are believed to have originated, 500 to 600 million years ago, from the hemichordates — a family of worm-like creatures who spend their lives burrowing in the ocean ooze, whose modern version is the acorn worm. The earliest true vertebrates — the *Agnatha*, or jawless fish — show up in the Ordovician, 500 million years ago. As we move up through the geologic column towards more recent times, the fossil record slowly becomes more complete. Lungfish make their first, gasping sorties on to dry land, and in the late Devonian, about 400 million years ago, the first four-legged amphibians, or *Tetrapods*, became established. True reptiles appear in the Carboniferous, 350 million years before the present (BP). The great glaciations of the Permian all but wiped out these gains, extinguishing more than fifty per cent of all life forms. But enough survived, and the earliest, probably egg-laying, mammals appear in the Triassic, 200 million years BP. The first recorded placental was a shrew-like insectivore from the upper Cretaceous, less than 100 million years BP. A forebear of ours, this creature was closely related to rodents and to the soon-to-be early primates; if not quite a rat, our direct ancestor was almost certainly a shrew.

The end of the Cretaceous, 65 million years BP, witnessed another world-wide, cataclysmic extinction of life forms. Many species were either extinguished or severely reduced in numbers; the reign of the dinosaurs was over. At latest count there are said to be *ninety* theories trying to account for their extinction. Most endearing, perhaps, is one which claims that, after a sudden change in flora, the monster lizards died of constipation. More convincing is the view that they succumbed to catastrophic world-wide climatic changes following the Earth's collision with a large (30km diameter) meteor.

At about that time, and helped, no doubt, by the appearance of concentrated foodstuffs — the first true seed-bearing, flowering plants — the still primitive mammals multiplied and prospered. The age of mammals, and ours, was heralded by flowers . . .

Thereafter, our family tree fills out rapidly — from tree-shrews and tarsiers through a series of ape-like hominid bones from Africa, India and Europe, to the Australopithecines of East Africa of two to five million years BP, and hence to our own genus *Homo*.

Dates appear, still, a trifle uncertain; nomenclatures vary. Over a time span of four million years or so there have been several Australopithecines — creatures more or less half way up, or down, the ladder between humans and apes — and a series of *Homo* species: H. *afarensis*, H. *habilis*, H. *erectus*, H. *Neanderthalis* and us, H. *sapiens*. Current thinking gives us an African origin (Australopithecus, H. *habilis* and *afarensis*). H. *erectus*, an unprepossessing creature by our standards, with heavy beetling brows, a sharply receding forehead, a huge jaw and powerful neck muscles appeared about one and a half million years ago and is almost certainly our ancestor. A few hundred thousand years ago *erectus*, *neanderthalis* and *sapiens* may have coexisted and, perhaps, interbred. All made stone tools whose sophistication increased through the millenia. The distinctions between species, however, are drawn mainly on anatomical grounds. The last important step, from *erectus* to *sapiens*, is taken to be the development of the brain; whereas changes in skeleton, teeth, jaw and cranial thickness also took place, it is the growth of the brain, from some 900 cc to 1300 cc, which anthropologists have used as the final and true measure of our humanity. In geological terms, this increase was sudden; it corresponded to the development, over a hundred thousand years or so, of the neocortex — the outer, essentially human layer of our brain. One can, at this stage, only speculate as to the causes of this very rapid evolution. A popular theory is that it had to do with language. For millions of years our ancestral hunters must have been, of necessity, social creatures. The groups may have been small — no more, perhaps, than extended families; but to hunt they had to include a number of able-bodied adults. Communication was vital;* the development of increasingly sophisticated languages would have had real survival value for these groups — and for the species as a whole. So it has been suggested that the growth of *Homo*'s brain may have gone apace with the use of more complex language. Language, thought and sensibility must have developed together; they led to the artists who created the wall paintings of Lascaux fifteen thousand years ago, to the Megalithic astronomers who built the great stone monuments of Brodgar and Carnac, and to us — '*Animal symbolicum*',[9] whose written records of religion and science begin in Sumer, Babylon and Egypt.

These two tales — the inflationary universe and the evolution of life on Earth — make up, together, our modern myth of Genesis. Other discoveries have fleshed out the story. Thus the birth of the solar system, which is now seen to have condensed out of a cloud of cosmic gas and debris about 4.6 billion years ago. And geology — the history of our planet — was revolutionized in the 1960s by the discovery of *plate tectonics*. One of the truly great achievements of twentieth century science, it has explained all major terrestrial features — mountain ranges, ocean basins, volcanoes, island arcs, seismic zones — in terms of forces created by the drifting and colliding of continent-sized crustal plates dragged along by currents in the underlying, viscuous mantle.

Like the Old Testament version, we may see all this as the first chapter of a great book — the book of science, the longest and perhaps the greatest of all human works. With Darwin, we

---

* Not necessarily *during* the hunt — to imply this, Hacking suggests, is unwise: 'Scholars who favour such rubbish have evidently never ploughed a field or stalked game, where silence is the order of the day . . .'[18]

may say: there is grandeur in this view of the world. Yet this, its opening chapter, is bleak.

The inflationary universe offers us a cosmos which arose by chance, and needs no maker. Evolutionary theory tells us that our planet's teeming life was created not by design, but by random forces. We, who have thought ourselves possessed of immortal souls, the apple of God's eye, the pride, joy and centre of the universe, are now relegated to an insignificant speck of a planet in a cosmos vast beyond comprehension, our bodies and brains mere colonies of cells, molded by an endless regression of chance events. No master plan had us or our universe in mind. Yet, dismal as this story sounds, we must remember that *we* are the storytellers *and* the interpreters. How we interpret it — as individuals or as a culture — is up to us. Which takes us into new seas of thought.

'Science,' says the philosopher Mary Midgeley, 'opens into metaphysics' — deep waters these, uneasy reaches where science and religion meet, a theme she explores in her book on *Evolution as Religion*.[3] Many scientists, like the geneticist Dobzhansky whom she quotes, would claim that, ideally, science and religion are separate — one deals with facts, the other with meaning. This, probably, is true for some who subscribe fully to a faith, such as Judaism or Christianity, whilst also understanding, or being involved with, the scientific world view. Yet the separation seems artificial since some of the 'factual' material of one field (Genesis, miracles) may overlap with that of the other (cosmology, physics): one way or another, science and holy writ *must* interact. Furthermore, and more significantly, even a totally atheistic scientist like, say, Monod, who states that the universe is meaningless, is thereby offering us an *interpretation* of the scientific cosmology — an interpretation which is, of necessity, itself an act of faith. It is no more factual or true than one which assumes that, behind all this, lies a hidden mind or God whom we have yet to find. Both views are matters of faith. In this respect, at least, the difference between a scientific or a religious *weltanschauung* no longer seems so great. Science and religion may have more in common than many, perhaps, are prepared to admit.

In pursuing analogies between science and religion one must, clearly, also consider the ethical problem. Together with a cosmology and a sense of meaning, traditional religions offer the faithful a moral code — explicit ideas of good and evil, prescriptions for a worthy life. Can science fill this role? In this delicate terrain we must tread with diffidence. I believe the answer to this question depends on the spirit in which it is asked.

Toulmin[10] convinces me that, on strictly philosophical, logical grounds, the answer must be *no*: any effort to construct a value system from scientific fact always introduces tacit, non-scientific value judgments of its own, and the resulting ethical system becomes trans-scientific. An example of this is Julian Huxley's *Evolutionary Ethics*, a system he attempts to base solely on the facts of biological evolution which, he claims:

> . . . assigns higher and lower degrees of value, the higher values being those which are more intrinsically or more permanently satisfying, or involve a greater degree of perfection . . . In other words, it is ethically right to aim at whatever will promote the increasingly full realization of increasingly higher values.

Whose idea of perfection? Whose higher values? And what of love and compassion? To arrive at these judgments from biological evolution we must first *interpret* the facts; such interpretations will, inevitably and in all cases, bring in individual and extraneous *value* judgments. As Toulmin writes: 'We all draw our own, different moral conclusions from the progress of the cosmic bandwagon.'

Nevertheless, such critical examination of the roots of one's faith is uncommon. The faithful, whatever their religion, tend to accept the rules without inquiring into their internal consistency. On this level, the answer to the question may well be: yes, why not? After all, systems like Huxley's, or Monod's ascetic ethic of objectivity,[11] whatever their actual, subjective roots, appear to offer acceptable prescriptions, and the solace that, in accepting a 'scientific' ethic, one is in tune with the times — jumping on to what looks like a real 'cosmic bandwagon'.

Perhaps, then, there are grounds for claiming that science *is* a new religion. World-wide, organized, it offers a cosmology transcending national and cultural boundaries. It has its own rigid orthodoxies, its creation myth, its high priests, its sinners and its saints. Faith in science is probably more widely distributed, more powerful and unshakeable than in any other of today's religions — and its cosmology is more factual.

Science has one last decisive feature in common with the great religions of this world. The sad truth is that, barring a minority, people have never believed in something simply on evidence that it was, in any sense of the word, 'true'. Dostoievsky's Grand Inquisitor put it this way: humanity wants neither the truth, nor the freedom that it gives — it wants *miracles, mystery* and *authority*. Dostoievsky understood full well that these have always been, and continue to be, the touchstones of mass religious faith. But miracles, mystery and authority are all about *power* — the power of gods, or of their representatives on earth, to order, punish, reward, create, heal and destroy. And science offers all of this, and more, on a gigantic scale — endless miracles, dependable, every-day miracles and power, trips to the moon, antibiotics, instant communication, live television halfway around the globe, computers, nuclear weapons. This power — unprecedented in our history — is the ultimate justification of our faith in science. Bacon's dictum that knowledge gives power now finds itself strangely inverted: today, *power is the validation of knowledge*.

Traditional Baconian faith postulates a causal relationship between advances in science and technological progress: it sees technology, largely, as the fruit of science. The modern *inversion* lies in further assuming that this fruit — these miracles — give proof of the validity of scientific knowledge. This can lead to absurd conclusions — for instance, to the idea that *other* forms of knowledge are invalid or, at best, inferior, a point of view encapsulated in 1965 by I.I. Rabi, one of America's most influential post-Second World War scientist-politicians, who once opined that:

> The arts are certainly central to life. Yet they are not the kind of thing that will inspire men to push on to new heights . . . Even the words of Shakespeare, which are essentially an exploration of human character, are really wonderful, glorified gossip.[12]

Dismissive of most of what is best in our human mindscape such postures are caricatures — careless and destructive. A parallel may be drawn with traditional attitudes towards our *physical* environment. I am reminded, in particular, of a passage from Lopez's *Arctic Dreams* — a marvellous book describing the ecology and history of the Canadian Arctic, in which the author comments on the despoliation of the landscape by the oil and mining interests, and on the views expressed by men working in the field:

> Whatever strong men could accomplish against the elements in such a place, they insisted, was inherently right. The last words of many of these discussions, whether they were delivered quizzically, cynically or in disbelief, were summary — what else is it good for?[13]

Simplistic? Yes, but no more so than Rabi's sentiments, to which they are close kin.

To be fair, many now take exception to such values — in the mines and in the oil fields, as in science. We are becoming less trustful of technology and science. *We know that knowledge and power must be tempered by wisdom: 'But where shall wisdom be found?'*

Notes and Bibliography

Chapter 1.   THE AGE OF EINSTEIN
1.   R.W. Clark, *Einstein, The Life and Times*, World Publishing, 1971.
2.   Abraham Pais, *'Subtle is the Lord . . .'*, The Science and the Life of Albert Einstein. Oxford University Press, 1982.
3.   Banesh Hoffman, *Albert Einstein, Creator and Rebel*. Viking Press, New York, 1972.
4.   Jacob Bronowski, *The Ascent of Man*, BBC, 1976.
5.   Barbara Tuchman, *A Distant Mirror*. Penguin, 1979.

Chapter 2.   THE AGE OF UNCERTAINTY
1.   E.F. Schumacher, *Small is Beautiful*, Abacus 1974.
2.   Immanuel Kant, *The Critique of Pure Reason*, Transl. Max Muller, Anchor Books, 1966.
3.   R.G. Harrison and D.J. Biswas, Chaos in Light, *Nature*, **321**, 394–401, 22 May 1987
4.   J.J. Tribbia and R.A. Anthes, The Scientific Basis of Modern Weather Prediction, *Science*, **237**, 493-499, 31 July 1987.
5.   Jaimes Gleick, *Chaos-making a new science*, Heinemann, 1988.
6.   Ian Stewart, *Does God Play Dice?*, Basil Blackwell, 1989.
7.   W.S. Broecker, Unpleasant Surprises in the Greenhouse, *Nature*, **328**, 123-126, 9 July 1987.
8.   Epicurus, Letter to Menoeceus, transl. C. Bailey in *Epicurus: The Extant Remains* (Clarendon, Oxford, 1926).

Chapter 3.   OF SCIENCE AND METHOD
1.   A. Einstein, in *Albert Einstein Philosopher Scientist*, ed. P.A. Schlipp, p. 684, The Library of Living Philosophers Inc., Evanston, Illinois, 1949.
2.   I. Tolstoy, *James Clerk Maxwell, A Biography*, p. 85, Chicago University Press, 1983 and Canongate Publishing, Edinburgh, 1981.
3.   P.W. Bridgman, *Reflections of a Physicist*, p. 278, Philosophical Library, New York, 1950.

4.   Ian Hacking, *Representing and Intervening*, p. 152, Cambridge University Press, Cambridge, 1983.

5.   Paul Feyerabend, *Science in a Free Society*, p. 98, Verso, London, 1982.

6.   Paul Feyerabend, *Philosophy of Science: A Subject with a Great Past*, from *Historical and Philosophical Perspectives in Science*, ed. R. Stuewer, p. 172, 1970.

7.   G. Sarton, *A History of Science, Ancient Science through the Golden Age of Greece*, p. 216, Harvard University Press, 1952.

8.   Aristotle, *Posterior Analysis*, quoted by T.E. Jones, *A History of Philosophy, The Classical Mind*, 2nd. ed., p. 253, 1969.

9.   Paul Feyerabend, *loc. cit* (6), p. 159.

10. Ian Hacking, *loc. cit* (4), p. 187.

11. Francis Bacon, *Novum Organum, The Works of Francis Bacon*, ed. J. Spedding, R.L. Ellis, D.D. Heath, Longman & Co., London, v.IV,I, sec. 25, (1868).

12. *Ibid* I, secs 18 & 36.

13. Hilary Putnam, in *Me i of Ideas*, ed. Bryan Magee, p. 232, BBC Publications 1978.

14. René Descartes, *Principles of Philosophy*, in *The Philosophical Works of Descartes*, transl Haldane and Ross, Vol. I, pp. 264-267, Cambridge University Press, 1931.

15. David Hume, *A Treatise of Human Nature*, ed. L.A. Selby-Bigge III,ii,l, Clarendon Press, Oxford, 1896.

16. Bertrand Russell, *History of Western Philosophy*, p. 646, George Allen & Unwin Ltd., 1962.

17. Immanuel Kant, *Critique of Pure Reason*, Transl Max Muller, p. 419, Anchor Books, 1966.

18. Ian Hacking, *loc. cit* (4), p. 43.

19. Paul Feyerabend, *Against Method*, p. 168, Verso, London, 1979.

20. Ian Hacking, *loc. cit* (4), p. 43.

21. Karl Popper, The Logic of Scientific Discovery, Basic Books, New York, 1959, p. 54.

22. Imre Lakatos, *History of Science and its Rational Reconstruction*, in Method and Appraisal in the Physical Sciences, ed. Colin Howson, p. 35, Cambridge University Press, 1976.

23. T.S. Kuhn, *Logic of Discovery or Psychology of Research*, in *Criticism and the Growth of Knowledge* (ed. Imre Lakatos and Alan Musgrave) p. 7, Cambridge University Press, 1970.

24. *Ibid* p. 9.

25. T.S. Kuhn, *The Structure of Scientific Revolutions*, Second ed. p. 158, Chicago University Press, 1970.

26. *Ibid* p. 166.

27. Margaret Masterman, *The Nature of a Paradigm*, in *Criticism and the Growth of Knowledge* (eds. Imre Lakatos and Alan Musgrave) p. 159, Cambridge University Press, 1970.

28. Paul Feyerabend, *Consolations for the Specialist*, in *Criticism and the Growth of Knowledge* (eds. Imre Lakatos and Alan Musgrave) p. 200, Cambridge University Press, 1970.

29. Imre Lakatos, *Falsification and the Methodology of Scientific Research Programmes*, in *Criticism and the Growth of Knowledge*, (eds. Imre Lakatos and Alan Musgrave), p. 93, Cambridge University Press, 1970.

30. R. Dawkins, *What was all the Fuss about?*, *Nature*, vol. 316, p. 683-684, 22 August 1985.

31. Paul Feyerabend, *On the Critique of Scientific Reason*, in *Method and Appraisal in the Physical Sciences*, ed. Colin Howson, p. 314n, Cambridge University Press, 1976.

32. Paul Feyerabend, *loc. cit* (19), p. 112.

33. Paul Feyerabend, *loc. cit* (5), p. 183.

34. *Ibid* p. 73.

35. Paul Feyerabend, *loc. cit* (19) p. 26.

36. Paul Feyerabend, Realism, Rationalism and Scientific Method, Cambridge Univ. Press, 1981, p. xiii.

Chapter 4.   THE BEGINNINGS

1. T.P. Ray, The winter Solstice Phenomenon at Newgrange, Ireland: Accident or Design? Nature, 26 January 1989, p. 342.

2. George Sarton, *A History of Science*. Ancient Science through the Golden Age of Greece, Harvard University Press, 1952.

3. S.F. Mason, *A History of the Sciences*, Collier Books, 1977.

4. Bertrand Russell, *History of Western Philosophy*, George Allen and Enwin, 1962.

5. M.I. Finley, ed., *The Legacy of Greece*, Clarendon, 1981 (Bernard Williams: Philosophy)

Chapter 5.   ATHENS

1. Bertrand Russell, *History of Western Philosophy*, George Allen and Unwin, 1962.

2. Xenophon, Memorabilia, quoted by G. Sarton in ref. 5.

3. E.M. Forster, *Aspects of the Novel*, Pelican, 1975.

4. W.T. Jones, *The Classical Mind — A History of Western Philosophy*, Vol. I, Harcourt, Brace & World, 1969.

5. G. Sarton, *A History of Science*. Ancient Science through the Golden Age of Greece, Harvard University Press, 1952.

6. P. Feyerabend, *Science in a Free Society*, Verso, 1978.

230 THE KNOWLEDGE AND THE POWER

7. Mary Renault, *The Nature of Alexander*. Penguin, 1984.
8. J.D. Bernal, *Science in History*, Pelican, 1969.
9. Bertrand Russell, An outline of Intellectual Rubbish, in *Unpopular Essays*, Simon and Schuster, New York, 1950.
10. G.E.R. Lloyd, Science and Mathematics, in *The Legacy of Greece*, M.I. Finley, ed., Clarendon, 1981.

Chapter 6.   ALEXANDRIA
1. G. Sarton, *A History of Science*, Hellenistic Science and Culture in the Last Three Centuries BC, Harvard University Press, 1959.
2. Plutarch, The Life of Marcellus, quoted by G. Sarton in ref. 1.
3. Edward Gibbon, *The Decline and Fall of the Roman Empire* (D.M. Low abridg.) Chatto and Windus, 1978.
4. W.T. Jones, *The Medieval Mind — A History of Western Philosophy*, Vol. II, Harcourt, Brace and World, 1969.
5. G. Sarton, *Introduction to the History of Science*, Vol. I, Carnegie Inst. of Washington, 1968.
6. S.F. Mason, *A History of the Sciences*, Collier Books, 1977.

Chapter 7.   TRANSITION
1. G. Sarton, *Introduction to the History of Science*, Vol. I, Carnegie Inst. of Washington, 1968.
2. G. Sarton, *Introduction to the History of Science*, Vol. III, Carnegie Inst. of Washington, 1968.
3. R.W. Southern, *Robert Grosseteste*, Clarendon, 1986.
4. W.T. Jones, *The Medieval Mind* — A History of Western Philosophy, Vol. II, Harcourt, Brace and World, 1969.
5. J. Huizinga, *The Waning of the Middle Ages*, Penguin, 1968.
6. Steward Easton, *Roger Bacon and His Search for a Universal Science*, Blackwell, Oxford, 1952.
7. A.C. Crombie, *Augustine to Galileo*, The History of Science AD 400-1650, Falcon Press, 1952.

Chapter 8.   REBIRTH
1. G. Bernard Wood, *Yorkshire*. B.T. Batsford Ltd., London, 1967.
2. David H. Pill, *The English Reformation 1529-58*, University of London Press Ltd., 1973.
3. T.E. Jones, From Hobbes to Hume, *A History of Western Philosophy* Vol. III, Harcourt, Brace and World, 1969.
4. Arthur Koestler, *The Sleepwalkers*, Penguin, 1969.
5. I.B. Cohen, *Revolution in Science*, Belknap Press (Harvard University Press), Boston, 1985.

6.   Bertrand Russell, *History of Western Philosophy*, George Allen and Unwin, 1962.

Chapter 9.   GALILEO
1.   Herbert Butterfield, *The Origins of Modern Science*, Bell and Hyman, 1985.
2.   Arthur Koestler, *The Sleepwalkers*, Pelican, 1969.
3.   Galileo, letter to Bellisario Vinta, quoted by S. Drake, ref. 5.
4.   S. Weinberg, Science as a Liberal Art, in Societal Issues, Scientific Viewpoints, Margaret Strom ed., American Institute of Physics, 1987.
5.   Stillman Drake, Discoveries and Opinions of Galileo, Doubleday Anchor Books, New York, 1957.
6.   Paul Feyerabend, *Against Method*, Verso, London, 1979.
7.   Galileo, Dialogue Concerning the Two Chief World Systems, Transl. S. Drake, University of California Press, Berkeley, 1953.
8.   Pietro Redondi, *Galileo: Heretic*, Princeton University Press, 1987.
9.   Joseph Pitt, Friends in High Places, The Sciences, New York Academy of Science, January-February 1988.
10.   Galileo, *Two New Sciences*, quoted by S. Drake, ref. 5.
11.   Jacob Bronowski, *The Ascent of Man*, BBC, 1976.

Chapter 10.   NEWTON AND THE ENLIGHTENMENT
1.   Richard S. Westfall, *Never at Rest*, A Biography of Newton, Cambridge University Press, 1980.
2.   Herbert Butterfield, *The Origins of Modern Science*, Bell and Hyman, 1985.
3.   D. Diderot, The Stocking Machine, from Complete Works, Vol. 6.
4.   Isaiah Berlin, *The Age of Enlightenment*, Oxford pbck, 1956.
5.   Lloyd A. Brown, The Longitude, in The Story of Maps from *The World of Mathematics* Vol. 2, Simon and Schuster, New York, 1956.
6.   James R Newman, Commentary on Pierre Simon de Laplace in *The World of Mathematics*, Vol. 2, Simon and Schuster, New York, 1956.
7.   G. Buffon, Of Animals Common to Both Continents, from *Histoire Naturelle des Quadrupèdes* IX, 1761. ·

Chapter 11.   THE AGE OF CERTAINTY
1.   J.D. Bernal, *Science in History*, Pelican, 1969.
2.   S.F. Mason, *A History of the Sciences*, Collier Books, 1977.
3.   S. Toulmin, *The Return to Cosmology*, University of California Press, 1982.

4.   Harold Spencer Jones, John Couch Adams and the Discovery of Neptune, from *The World of Mathematics*, ed. J.R. Newman, Vol. 2, Simon and Schuster, New York, 1956.

5.   Jacob Bronowski, *The Ascent of Man*, BBC, 1976.

6.   I. Tolstoy, *James Clerk Maxwell*, A Biography, Canongate Publishing, Edinburgh, 1981 and Chicago University Press, 1983.

7.   Richard Feynman, *Lectures on Physics* by Feynman, Leighton and Sands, Addison Wesley, 1963.

8.   Bernard Jaffe, *Mendeleyev*, from the World of Mathematics, Vol. 2, ed. J.R. Newman, Dimon and Schuster, New York, 1956.

9.   J.H. Brooke, in *The Crisis of Evolution*, The Open University Press, 1974.

10.   S.J. Gould, *Ever Since Darwin*, W.W. Norton & Co., New York, 1977. See in particular the fourth essay, entitled *Darwin's Untimely Burial* — it gives a lucid and detailed account of the subtle (but false) accusation of tautology that is sometimes levelled at Darwin's theory.

Chapter 12.   THE POSTMODERN WORLD

1.   D.S. Greenberg, *The Politics of Pure Science*, The New American Library, 1967.

2.   J.K. Galbraith, *The New Industrial State*, Penguin, 1974.

3.   Mary Midgeley, *Evolution as Religion*, Methuen, 1985.

4.   P.C.W. Davies and J. Brown, eds., *Superstrings, A theory of everything?* Cambridge University Press, 1988.

5.   Stephen Hawking, *A Brief History of Time*, Bantam Press, 1988.

6.   Carl Sagan, *Cosmos*, Random House, 1980.

7.   Freeman Dyson, *Origins of Life*, Cambridge University Press, 1985.

8.   Ian Hacking, *Representing and Intervening*, Cambridge University Press, 1983.

9.   Ernst Cassirer, *An Essay on Man*, Yale University Press, 1944.

10.   Stephen Toulmin, *The Return to Cosmology*, University of California Press, 1982.

11.   Jacques Monod, *Le Hasard et la Nécessité*, Seuil, Paris, 1970.

12.   I.I. Rabi, Science and Technology in *The Impact of Science and Technology*. eds. Warner, Morse and Eichner (Columbia University Press, 1965).

13.   Barry Lopez, *Arctic Dreams*, Picador, 1986.

Index

/